INTRODUCTION 1

UNIT 1 ACTIVITY AND YOU
Introductory unit; reasons for participation and skills; different types of fitness 2

UNIT 2 SPORT AND SOCIETY
Reasons for participation: leisure; competition; careers; sponsorship; money 4

UNIT 3 PHYSICAL ACTIVITIES ON OFFER
Types of physical activities; similarities and differences; object and rules; conduct and etiquette; judging and recording 8

UNIT 4 WHO'S WHO IN PHYSICAL ACTIVITY
Different roles in physical activities: spectators; administrators; organising bodies; coaches; performers 14

UNIT 5 WE ARE THE SAME!
People with special needs; examples of special needs; experiencing problems; involving everyone in physical activity 18

UNIT 6 ACTIVITIES AND SPECTATORS
What makes a physical activity entertaining? changing the rules; spectator behaviour; spectator attendances 20

UNIT 7 GEARED UP
Equipment; reasons for changes in sporting equipment: safety; fashion; performance 23

UNIT 8 SAFETY IN PHYSICAL ACTIVITIES
Accidents in sports; avoiding accidents; safety; equipment; personal responsibility 25

UNIT 9 SPORT AND DRUGS
The problems of drugs and sport; reasons for cheating; effects of drugs; dangers to health; detection 27

UNIT 10 SPORT AND POLITICS
Political issues affecting sport 30

UNIT 11 HOW SKILFUL ARE YOU?
Defining a skill; the skilful performer; closed and open skills; co-ordination; judgement; effectiveness; reaction time; creativity; skill selection 32

UNIT 12 TECHNIQUE AND STYLE
Techniques; selecting a technique; breaking down techniques; style; stylish performers 35

UNIT 13 EXPRESSIVE MOVEMENT
Expressing emotions through movement; imagination; types of body movement 38

UNIT 14 MAY THE FORCE BE WITH YOU!
Body mechanics; types of force; centre of gravity (CoG); CoG and physical skills; balance and stability; developing techniques 40

UNIT 15 IT'S ALL IN THE MIND
Mental preparation; concentration; personality types; motivation 44

UNIT 16 PRACTICE MAKES PERFECT
Co-ordination; senses; kinaesthetic; feedback; practice 46

PHYSICAL EDUCATION

in action

P Black
W Cruickshank
& D Ledingham

Nelson

17 TACTICS — Importance of tactics; examples from sport; making tactical decisions — 49

18 COACHING AND LEARNING — Role of the coach; coaching methods; giving feedback; structuring practice — 51

19 SIZE AND SHAPE — Body shapes; suitability for activities; power to weight ratio — 53

20 THE BODY'S MOVING FRAMEWORK — Structure of skeletal framework; function of framework; antagonistic muscle action; flexion; extension; adduction; abduction — 56

21 CONTROLLING YOUR MOVEMENT — Structure of voluntary nervous system; central and peripheral nervous system; motor units; reflex action — 59

22 WARM-UP AND COOL DOWN — Importance of warm-up; structure of warm-up; relationship to flexibility; cooling down — 61

23 FITNESS OVERVIEW — Health related fitness; performance related fitness; fitness profile; constituents of fitness — 63

24 FLEXIBILITY — Flexibility tests; importance of flexibility; flexibility restrictions — 67

25 YOUR BODY'S FOOD REFINERY AND POWER SOURCE — Carbohydrates; fats; proteins; carbohydrate metabolism; lactic acid; aerobic respiration; anaerobic respiration — 70

26 THE OXYGEN TRANSPORT SYSTEM — Cardio-respiratory system; pulmonary circulation; systemic circulation; vital capacity; stroke volume; heart rate — 73

27 DEVELOPING CARDIOVASCULAR ENDURANCE — Benefits of endurance training; resting heart rate; maximal heart rate; training zones; altitude training; blood doping; interval training — 79

28 STRENGTH: MOVE IT OR HOLD IT — Definition of strength; activities requiring strength; isometric and isotonic strength — 76

29 DEVELOPING STRENGTH — Training systems; isotonic and isometric exercises; principle of overload; duration; frequency — 81

30 MUSCULAR ENDURANCE — Relationship to strength; definition; repetitions; circuit training — 84

31 POWER IS 'FAST STRENGTH' — Definition of power; importance of power; explosive power — 87

32 SPORTS INJURIES — Fractures; muscle tears; dislocation; connective tissue injuries; concussion; precautions; treatment; chronic injuries — 89

Index — 92

CONTENTS

PHYSICAL EDUCATION

in action

Thomas Nelson and Sons Ltd
Nelson House Mayfield Road
Walton-on-Thames Surrey
KT12 5PL UK

Nelson Blackie
Wester Cleddens Road
Bishopbriggs
Glasgow
G64 2NZ UK

Thomas Nelson Australia
102 Dodds Street
South Melbourne
Victoria 3205 Australia

Nelson Canada
1120 Birchmount Road
Scarborough Ontario
M1K 5G4 Canada

© P. Black, D. Ledingham and W. Cruickshank 1991

First published by Blackie and Son Ltd 1991
ISBN 0-216-92632-7

This edition published by Thomas Nelson and Sons Ltd 1993

I(T)P Thomas Nelson is an International

Thomson Publishing Company

I(T)P is used under licence
ISBN 0-17-438672-9
NPN 9 8 7 6 5 4 3
Printed in China

ACKNOWLEDGEMENTS

Andrew Lambert 2 (top right, bottom left), 3, 10 (left), 14 (left and right), 23 (bottom left and bottom right), 25 (top and bottom), 26 (left), 34 (right), 42 (left and right), 54 (bottom left), 59, 62 (top and bottom), 64, 66 (right), 67 (left, top right and bottom right), 68, 70 (left, top right, middle right and bottom right), 79 (left), 86

Bob Thomas Sports Photography 2 (bottom right), 5, 6 (bottom), 7, 18 (left and right), 22, 23 (top left and top right), 25 (middle), 27, 30, 34 (left), 35, 38 (left, middle and right), 39, 40, 46, 47 (top left, bottom left and top right), 54 (top left), 66 (left), 71 (top and bottom), 79 (right), 87 (top left, top right, bottom left and bottom right)

Supersport 2 (top left), 10 (right), 26 (right), 43, 51

Allsport 11, 82 (top and bottom)

Coca-Cola Great Britain 6 (top). "Coca-Cola" and "Coke" are registered tradmarks which identify the same product of The Coca-Cola Company

This book has been written for students following an examination course in physical education at Standard Grade or GCSE level, but it will also be very useful as an introductory text throughout the whole sphere of physical education. It is highly illustrated with photographs and diagrams, and is suitable for a wide range of abilities.

As its title suggests, this is a textbook which is rooted in physical activity and practical performance. The approach adopted throughout the book is one where information is directly related to practice, instead of being presented as facts and principles for its own sake. By selecting this refreshingly new approach, it is intended that the text will complement and supplement the practical experiences to be enjoyed during physical education, rather than replace them.

The content is set out in three inter-related sections:

- You, physical activity, sport and society
  (red section)
- Sporting skills, performance and improvements
  (orange section)
- Your body, fitness and training
  (yellow section).

A section is made up of a number of units, each one consisting of a manageable chunk of information presented in a logically progressive order. The student can follow the order of units as laid down, or select units as interest or class work dictates. More complex information, for the more able, is included within 'info boxes', and each unit concludes with a brief summary of the main points covered for immediate reinforcement.

This structure of three sections of easily digested units will allow a flexible approach to learning. Whichever strategy is adopted, we hope that this book will enhance your enjoyment of the subject of physical education.

ACTIVITY AND YOU

People of all ages and abilities enjoy taking part in physical activities. There are many reasons why they choose to do so. Possible reasons may include:

● to be the best in the world;
● to make money;
● for fun and enjoyment;
● to become fit, and to keep fit;
● to make friends;
● as a way of using their leisure time;
● to enjoy competition;
● to be creative and expressive.

TASK 1

Look back at the pictures. Can you match each activity to a possible reason for doing it? (You may find that some activities can be matched to more than one reason.)

TASK 2

Now consider yourself: why do you take part in physical activity? Write down your reasons in your PE folder.

TASK 3

List all the different reasons to be found in your class, then discuss them. Which is the most popular reason? Why do you think this is?

ACTIVITIES AND SKILLS

All physical activities require **skills**. Running is a skill, so is turning on skis and catching a ball in cricket.

Some skills may be simple and easy to learn while others may be more complicated.

Some may be carried out on your own while others require you to work or cooperate with other people.

Some may be common to different activities while others may be specific to one activity.

ⓘ THOUGHT SPOT

Think of other examples which fit the three categories:
a) simple/complicated;
b) on your own/work with others;
c) specific skills/common skills.

All skills can be improved through practice. The most skilful performers spend hours and hours of time in practice and training (usually away from the 'public eye').

DIFFERENT TYPES AND LEVELS OF FITNESS

Different types of activity often require different types of fitness. For example, a weightlifter requires **strength**, a middle-distance runner needs **stamina** and an ice skater has to have good **flexibility**.

Sometimes, within the same activity, different levels of fitness are required. Take football as an example—youngsters having a playground kickabout during their school lunchbreak do not require the level of fitness that is needed by an international footballer.

SUMMARY

There are many different physical activities and many reasons why people take part in them.

Physical activities require skills. They may be:

● easy or difficult to learn;
● performed with other people, or on your own;
● common to more than one activity, or specific to only one.

The type of fitness needed depends on the activity. The level of fitness needed may depend on the reason for taking part.

SPORT AND SOCIETY

Nowadays, millions of people take part in an ever-growing number of activities.

There has been a dramatic increase in both the number of sports facilities and the range of activities available.

In particular, a number of individual activities have grown in popularity.

There are several reasons for the increase in the number of people who take part in physical activity—here are three of them.

1. Today more and more people are concerned about their health and the need to take regular exercise.
2. People have more free time to enjoy the many activities available.
3. Taking part in physical activity is a good way of meeting friends.

 **THOUGHT SPOT**

Can you think of other reasons?

THE IMPORTANCE OF WINNING

As well as those who take part in sport for fun, there are people who want to be the best in their chosen sport. They devote almost their whole lives to training and performing.

The importance placed on winning in sport can lead to problems, disadvantages and difficulties for some people.

What is said on the radio, TV or in the newspapers

Large amounts of prize money at stake

 Being chosen for your country

 Finding time to train as well as work

 Officials can be deceived

 Fans demanding success

 Not playing within the spirit of the game

 Some people bend or break the rules

Others may have had more help, for example with clothes or equipment, or money for travel

Opponents taking illegal drugs in training

TASK 1

Decide which of the pressures listed above apply to:
a) top performers;
b) amateurs;
c) everyone.

TASK 2

In which order do you think a top performer might list these pressures?

TASK 3

Contact an amateur sportsperson and find out:
a) what problems that person has to overcome to take part in that sport;
b) what help, if any, he or she receives.
Compare your findings with your classmates.

TASK 4

Identify the pressures above which could result in cheating. Can you find an example for each one?

MONEY AND SPORT

The growth in sports in recent years has provided jobs for coaches, administrators and support staff (e.g. caddies, canteen staff, lifeguards, groundsmen). All these people have to be paid.

Money for this is generated in many ways. For example, at sports centres you pay for the floor area or equipment that you use. Activities at a higher level often charge spectators money to watch. At the highest level, sport now receives large sums of money as a result of television and advertising.

Attractive and popular sports gain the attention of television.

Individuals and sports associations may receive money from television companies for allowing them to broadcast a game or event.

Businesses see televised sport as an excellent way of advertising. They either sponsor individuals and teams in return for their name/logo being displayed on clothing, or they pay for 'trackside' advertising when the event is televised.

This financial support is very welcome but it can also have unwelcome effects. Here are two examples.

1. The American football 'Superbowl'. It could be argued that this event is staged to suit the television companies. At certain points in the play, live transmission is stopped, and only resumes once the television advertisements are finished. Therefore play and viewing are not continuous.

2. The 1988 Olympic Games in Seoul. The American television company NBC paid large sums of money for the rights to televise and broadcast the Games. Time in Korea is 14 hours ahead of the eastern USA. NBC demanded that all athletics finals took place in the early morning (Korean time), which guaranteed prime time viewing figures in the late afternoon and early evening (USA time) but athletes had to alter sleep patterns and lifestyles in order to be able to perform at this unusual time.

Were the 1988 Olympic Games a festival of sport or a showcase for giant multinational companies? Although the Olympic venues were free of advertising, the Games were very much 'big business'.

The International Olympic Committee (IOC) gained most of its money from two sources:

1. the sale of television rights;
2. a sponsorship programme involving the Olympic emblem.

The marketing division of the IOC raised millions of dollars for the 1988 Games by selling the right to use the Olympic rings for marketing purposes to nine major corporations.

TASK 5

As any major sports event approaches (e.g. the Olympic Games, FIFA World Cup), note and collect examples of the 'official' products (camera film, fast food, soft drink, etc.).

TASK 6

Choose a team or club in your area, and find out how they are financed.

Barcelona '92

© 1988 COOB'92, S.A. All rights reserved ™

SUMMARY

The numbers taking part in physical activities are growing—concerns about health, more leisure time and the opportunity to meet friends are three of the reasons.

The emphasis placed on winning in sport can sometimes cause problems for those taking part.

Some physical activities provide jobs for people.

Selling television rights and advertising space are two ways in which sports can raise money.

Activities and events which attract large sums of money may have to meet certain demands made by whoever is supplying the money.

PHYSICAL ACTIVITIES ON OFFER

The Activity Route Map on pages 12 and 13 will help you:

a) recognise the form each activity takes;
b) understand the similarities and differences between activities.

It may also help you understand some of the reasons why you prefer doing one activity rather than another.

Look now at the Activity Route Map. Study it, and become familiar with its design. Begin at the 'start' point (bottom centre), and note how it splits into two routes—the right-hand route leads to 'collection of individuals' whilst the left-hand route leads to 'individual'. You may discover some words you have not come across before. Look up their meaning in a dictionary and write them in your PE folder. There is no rush: take your time.

TASK 1

Try tracing an activity. Let's use 'American football'. Place your index finger on the starting point. From here you can choose one of two routes, either 'collection of individuals' or 'individual'. American football is an activity which is performed by a collection of people, so you need to choose the right-hand route: trace your finger to 'collection of individuals'.

You will find two routes leading from this box. One leads to 'competitive' and the other to 'non-competitive'. American football is an activity where one team plays against another, so move your finger to the competitive box.

Here, you have three route choices: 'challenge', 'race' or 'display'. American football is certainly not a race (like rowing), nor is it a display (like ice dancing). Therefore it must be a challenge. Choose the route leading to 'challenge'.

You are now faced with two routes: 'missile' or 'no missile'. (A missile is anything that is hit, thrown, kicked, pushed, batted, struck, fired, etc.) Does American football have a missile? Of course it does—the ball. Choose the missile route: trace with your finger.

You are now faced with three routes: 'batting and fielding', 'ebb and flow' or 'target'. Each describes a different type of challenge. American football does not involve a 'batting team' and a 'fielding' team—so you can discount that category. Nor does it involve a target (as in curling), but it certainly 'ebbs and flows'—for example, one minute the Chicago Bears are attacking near the Miami Dolphins' end-zone, and the next, the Dolphins have gained 70 yards and the Bears are on the defensive. Trace the route to 'ebb and flow'.

Note: the 'can be affected'/'cannot be affected' choice does not appear because American football, like *all* competitive games, is an activity where your actions can directly affect how well your opponents perform.

The route now leads to either 'with implement' or 'no implement'. An implement is a piece of equipment other than clothing used for safety (for example, a hockey stick is an 'implement' whereas an American football helmet is 'clothing'). American football does not have implements—so you can trace the route through the 'no implement' box, where you are faced with another choice ; 'contact' or 'non contact'. American football is a high contact activity—so trace the route through the correct box until you face 'How success is measured'.

How success is measured concerns the objective of the challenge. It is either the reason behind participation or what the participants are trying to do.

You have two choices: 'objective points' or 'distance'. The objective of American football is to score points, so the correct choice will be 'objective points'.

The 'objective points' category splits into four choices. How are points scored in American football? The missile (the ball) is carried onto the area (the end-zone) for six points and then the ball is kicked over a bar for a further one point. So the 'into an area/over a line/into a goal' box is the correct choice.

You have now traced American football from start to finish. (If necessary, read through this section again, tracing with your finger as you read.)

TASK 2

Write the heading 'The Activity Route Map' in your PE folder. Now write a paragraph about American football, including all the categories through which its route passes. For example: 'American football is performed by a collection of individuals and is a competitive challenge involving a missile. This challenge . . .'.

TASK 3

Now it is your turn to trace by yourself. Trace your favourite activity from start to finish. Write a similar paragraph for this activity in your PE folder.

OBJECTIVE AND RULES

Each activity has an objective—what you are trying to do. How this is achieved can differ from activity to activity. For example, it might be to score a goal, or to be awarded maximum points, or to finish with the best time or distance.

 THOUGHT SPOT

Think of other examples for each of the three categories above.

Activities with a similar objective can be quite different in shape or form because of the rules. For example, in waterpolo, hockey and football, the object is to score a goal, but how this can be done is quite different because of the rules applied and the skills needed.

 THOUGHT SPOT

What are the major differences in these three activities with regard to goal scoring? (Think of implements, use of hands, etc.)

TASK 4

'Beat the goalkeeper' is the objective of all three activities. How do the rules of each determine the particular skills needed? (Before deciding, you may need to find out more about the rules for each activity.)

Each activity also has its own set of rules, restrictions and/or codes of conduct which allow the object to be achieved. Rules tell the performers what they can or cannot do, and also 'shape' the activity by determining the skills required.

Some skills develop as a result of certain rules. For example, the aim of the 'serve' in badminton is to land the shuttle in your opponent's service box.

The rules say:

● you must have both feet on the ground;
● you must hit the shuttle with an underarm action;
● the racket must make contact with the shuttle below the waist.

A second example comes from basketball. The 'tip-off' is used to start or restart a game. The rules say a 'jump ball' takes place when the ball is tossed between two opposing players. Each jumper must stand with his/her feet inside the half of the circle nearer his/her basket, with one foot nearer the line.

! THOUGHT SPOT

Can you think of skills in other games which have developed as a result of the rules and which are used to:
a) start a game?
b) score a point or goal?
c) attack or defend?

CHANGING THE RULES

Rules can be changed to take account of age, ability, and level of competition. Here are some examples.

1. A teacher may apply certain rules when introducing an activity. This helps beginners to understand the activity, to develop skills and to take part in a flowing game even though they are not following all the rules.

2. When people of different abilities take part in a competition, rules or conditions can be applied which give everyone an equal chance of winning (e.g. the handicap system in golf).

3. Some people may not wish to take part at a high level and the rules may be relaxed to suit the level of interest (e.g. four friends playing 'social' badminton).

4. Rules can be changed or modified to suit the level of ability (e.g. wheelchair basketball).

Some activities also expect fair play (sometimes called sportsmanship). For example, in cricket, bowling fast short-pitched balls (bouncers) that bounce off the pitch and fly upwards towards the top part of a batsman's body is considered unfair if they are used too often with the aim of frightening a batsman or causing him injury. It is not unfair to bowl bouncers—or even to bowl lots of them—at batsmen who can play them. The umpire only intervenes to caution the bowler when he feels they are being used too often in an intimidating way, or where the batsman does not have the skill to deal with them.

Spectators can also be expected to show courtesy to players, e.g. rugby spectators are expected to remain silent when a player is taking a kick at goal.

In some activities the rules forbid the use of certain items of equipment (to avoid unfair advantage). For example, the rules of hockey state that 'The head of the stick shall be curved and shall be of wood and should not be edged with or have any insets or fittings of metal.'

CONDUCT AND ETIQUETTE

Many activities have rules about how a team or individual should behave (often known as **etiquette**). Some of these rules are written down. Golf is a good example. Here is an extract from the rules.

> **Practice swings** - in taking practice swings players should avoid causing damage to the course, particularly the tees, by removing divots. No one should move, talk or stand close to, or directly behind, the ball when the player is addressing the ball or making a stroke.

JUDGING AND RECORDING

Equipment used to measure, time and record results is continually being improved. For example, the increasing use of electronic equipment in athletics means the result is:

● worked out very quickly;
● displayed to everyone very soon after the performance is over;
● more accurate.

🅘 THOUGHT SPOT
Think of other examples where the rules forbid the use of certain design features in equipment.

SUMMARY

Each activity has an **objective**.
There are many types of objective.
Rules 'shape' activities by stating how the objective will be achieved, and determine the skills needed.
Etiquette is important in some activities.

THE ACTIVITY ROUTE MAP

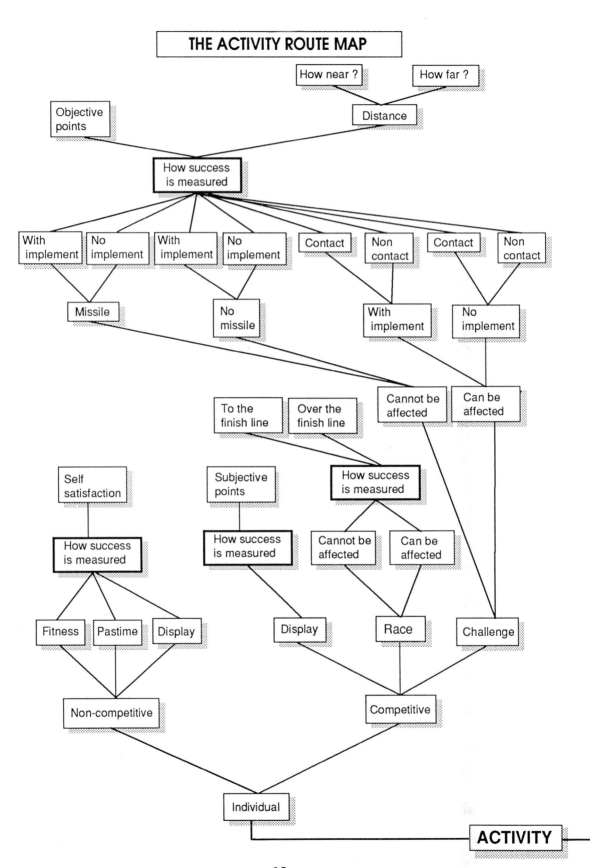

THE ACTIVITY ROUTE MAP

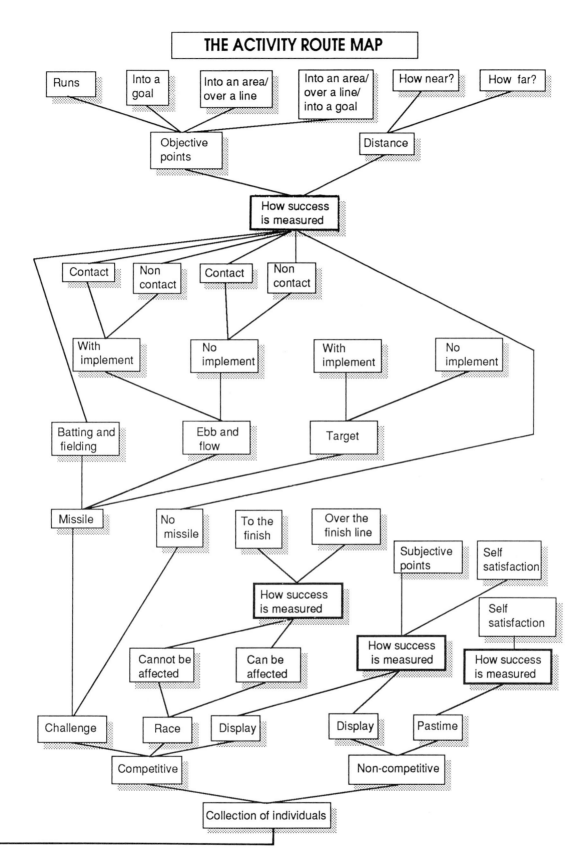

WHO'S WHO IN PHYSICAL ACTIVITY

In activities at a **higher level**, more roles are involved. In the photograph, two performers are tossing the coin, supervised by an official—the referee. In an activity, the official's role is often the next most obvious role after that of the performer's. The official makes sure that the activity is performed within the rules.

At the highest level, many more roles are involved. Some are obvious (e.g. the coach or trainer) whilst others are 'behind the scenes' (e.g. groundstaff).

Performers play a central role in any activity; without them, there cannot be an activity. Consider an example of an activity at a **low level**—a playground game of 'tig'. The pupils simply play the game—no one else is involved.

TASK 1

The list below contains a variety of roles which may be found whenever an activity at the highest level takes place.

tactician	coach
selector	referee
journalist	catering staff
judge	steward
equipment supplier	groundsman
linesman	manager
governing body	physiotherapist
director	performer
umpire	teacher
sponsor	recorder
doctor	organiser
greenkeeper	owner
choreographer	commentator
advertiser	timekeeper
chairman	trainer
starter	scorer
director	receptionist
committee member	sports centre staff
spectator	shopkeeper

Draw a table in your PE folder like the one on the top of the next page. Place each role listed above in its correct column. One example has been done for you.

Performers	Officials	Performance Assistants	Administrators	Preparation and Supply Staff	Observers
		tactician			

A CLOSER LOOK AT SUPPORT ROLES

1. The Administrator

An administrator is involved whenever any physical activity is 'organised'. Administrators range from volunteers, who spend an hour or two each week helping to 'run' a club, to the full-time paid employees of international governing bodies. There are many types of administrator—here are three examples.

Shirley is 32, and a teacher of physical education. She has been capped 52 times at senior-level netball. She has coached her club for the last four years, and the district team for the last two years.

Selection committee member

Andrew is a recently retired lawyer. He has been a member of his local golf club for thirty years, serving on the committee for the last fifteen years. A spell of five years on the committee of his local sports council makes him an experienced administrator.

Club secretary

Kashaf, 32 years old, has always been a keen hockey player, but recently gave up playing through injury. As captain in the past, he has served on the club committee. His experience will be valuable at district level.

District committee official

TASK 2

Consider the following list of tasks and decide which of the administrators described above might be involved in each:
a) coordinating the league fixtures;
b) dealing with applications for membership;
c) deciding upon competition rules;
d) arranging inter-club fixtures;
e) booking facilities;
f) organising coaching courses;
g) requesting grant for extension to clubhouse.

 THOUGHT SPOT

Can you think of other tasks for which an administrator might be responsible?

2. The Coach

Coaches are involved with individuals, clubs, district and national teams. The job of the coach is to prepare the performer(s) for competition.

A coach needs to think about:

- fitness and training;
- skills and skill level;
- tactics, strategies, sequences;
- motivation.

Questions a coach might ask are:

- How fit are my players?
- How fit do they need to be?

Once the coach knows the answers to these questions, he or she might test fitness levels, devise a suitable training programme, and supervise training sessions.

- What skills are needed in this activity?
- Which skills need improvement?

Once the coach knows the answers to these questions, he or she might be involved in improving skills through practices and drills.

- What are our strengths and weaknesses?
- What are theirs?
- How should we approach this game/event/ competition?

In order to answer these questions, a coach might watch opponents to assess their strengths and weaknesses. With this knowledge, and knowing the abilities of his or her own players, the coach will devise a suitable game plan (tactics).

- How can I make sure that the team plays at their best?

In preparation for the event, a coach will work on attitude, frame of mind, concentration level, etc.

Coaches play a very important role in many activities. Help can be obtained from The National Coaching Foundation to improve the quality of coaching.

SUPPORT ORGANISATIONS

1. The Sports Council

The Sports Council was set up in 1972 and plays a major role in the development of sport. The Council is made up of twelve members from sporting and sports administrative backgrounds who meet monthly to discuss Council business. The Sports Council is funded annually by the Government. There are separate councils for England, Scotland, Wales and Northern Ireland.

The Sports Council has four main aims:
a) to encourage people of all ages and abilities to participate in sport;
b) to increase the quality and quantity of sports facilities;
c) to improve sporting standards;
d) to provide information for and about sport to people (including local authorities and the governing bodies of sport, for example the Scottish Ski Council, or the British Canoe Union).

The Council provides grants to individuals for training, and to governing bodies for new sporting ventures. Applications for grants must include an explanation of how the money will be used.

The Council is also involved in special campaigns to promote sport. A Sport-for-All campaign was first started in the 1970s with the aim of encouraging people to take up a physical activity in their leisure time. The Sports Council also targets groups such as the disabled, ethnic minorities and the over 50s to encourage them to be more involved in sport.

The Council runs five National Sports Centres which are used:

- by national teams and individuals for training and competition;
- for coaching and administration;
- for 'try a sport' courses for the public.

The Sports Council has also set up local sports councils to bring together all those interested in sport in each community to discuss local 'needs'.

TASK 3

Find out the names and locations of the National Sports Centres and what facilities they have.

2. Central Council of Physical Recreation (CCPR)

Until the Sports Council was set up in 1972, the Central Council of Physical Recreation was responsible for the development of sport. It is still in existence and is made up of over 200 organisations. It offers advice and information to many people including the Sports Council.

3. National Playing Fields Association (NPFA)

The National Playing Fields Association was founded in 1926 and exists to promote the idea that land and facilities should be made available for people to make use of in sport and leisure.

4. British Olympic Association (BOA)

The British Olympic Association is the national Olympic committee responsible for the Olympic movement in Britain. One of its many duties is to look after the British team at the Olympic Games.

SUMMARY

Performers play the main role in physical activities.

The higher the level of performance, usually the greater the number and type of supporting roles.

The **roles** involved could be grouped under the following six headings: performers, officials, performance assistants, administrators, preparation and support assistants, observers.

A **coach** helps a performer prepare for the activity by developing his or her fitness, skills, tactics and motivation.

Sports councils aim to encourage participation, improve sporting standards, and build sports facilities.

WE ARE THE SAME!

A blind competitor being helped along in the London marathon

TASK 1

Answer the following questions.
1. Have you ever been treated like a child or someone who is stupid?
2. Have you ever wanted to take part in something but were prevented?
3. Have you ever been ignored by another person?
4. Have you ever felt that you are not being as fairly treated as other people?

TASK 2

If you answered 'yes' to any or all of the above questions touch the words below which described your feelings.

In doing Tasks 1 and 2 you may perhaps begin to get some idea about what it can be like to be a person with a **special need**. The main difference is that a person with a special need might have to answer 'yes' to questions like the ones in Task 1 many times every day.

INFO BOX

What is a special need?
All human beings have basic needs, such as eating, drinking and sleeping. Apart from our basic needs we have other needs such as friendship, encouragement, education and entertainment.

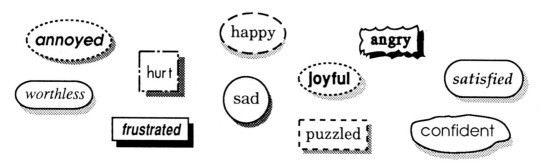

annoyed   happy   angry

hurt   joyful   satisfied

worthless   sad

frustrated   puzzled   confident

People with **special needs** have just the same needs as other people, but they also have additional needs which have to be met if they are going to take part on an equal footing with everyone else. People with special needs may suffer from:

a) cerebral palsy—this is a physically disabling condition, the most obvious feature of which is imperfect muscle coordination. It is caused by damage to a part of the brain which controls movement and posture. People with cerebral palsy can have a very wide range of intelligence but speech may be affected, even with the very intelligent;

b) blindness—some 'blind' people have an ability to see something even if it is only light, shade or colours;

c) deafness—some deaf people may be able to hear a little with the use of powerful hearing aids;

d) spina bifida—people with this disease may suffer lack of feeling or movement in the legs and lower body. This is due to the bones in the spine failing to join together, resulting in damage to the lower part of the spinal cord.

TASK 3

The point of the following tasks is to experience what it is like to live as a person with special needs.

1. Choose a friend, relative or partner and ask them to play the part of a receptionist at a sports centre. Without speaking or writing, communicate that you would like to book the swimming pool for yourself and fifteen of your friends on a Tuesday evening next month and find out whether or not the cafeteria will be open.

2. Blindfold yourself and, under the supervision of a friend or partner, try running in an open space well away from roads. Sprint 50 metres in a straight line and then run 800 metres following the voice of your partner. Which did you find easier?

3. With your teacher's permission, attempt to follow a PE lesson wearing headphones or ear plugs. How much did you understand?

4. Think of the route you travel every day from home to school or college. Imagine you have to make this journey in a wheelchair. How many obstacles such as kerbs, steps, buses, corners, slopes, would you have to overcome?

TALKING POINT

The statements below were made by people with special needs. What can you do within your school or community to give them the same chances that you have?

'I want the same opportunities.'

'Include me—don't cut me off.'

'Most of the time I don't need any help but if I sometimes do it doesn't make you better than me.'

'How would you feel if you were given less opportunities?'

'Treat me the same as anyone else—give me the same chance.'

'I can compete with people of the same ability— so do you.'

'I can enjoy taking part in sport just as much as you—does it really matter if I am not as good as you?'

'People say I can't take part or that I would spoil the fun. I know I am not able to take part in some activities because of my special need, but if you asked me I could perhaps help or become involved in some way.'

TASK 4

There are many activities which have been adapted to allow people with special needs to take part in them, e.g. wheelchair basketball.
By yourself, or with others, try to make up a physical activity which can be played by people without special needs and people with special needs at the same time.

ACTIVITIES AND SPECTATORS

Some activities are very popular and are well attended by spectators. The money which these spectators pay to watch may be a very important source of income for those involved.

TASK 1

In your PE folder make a list of the different ways in which activities can raise money.
How might this money be used?

Not everybody likes to attend 'live' sports events—some people prefer to watch them on television.

❗ THOUGHT SPOT

Why do you think some people prefer watching sport 'live', while others prefer to do their viewing on television?

Some activities can be more entertaining then others.

❗ THOUGHT SPOT

Why do you think spectators find some activities more appealing to watch then others?

The rules of some activities, for example squash, have been changed in the hope of making the activity more attractive and enjoyable for spectators. Other activities, for example orienteering, are not suitable for very large groups of spectators.

❗ THOUGHT SPOT

1. What change was made to the design of squash courts in the 1970s to make this game suitable for spectators?
2. What rule changes were made to 'Tele-squash' to make it more appealing to TV viewers?
3. Can you name one other activity with the same problem as orienteering?

WIMBLEDON WASHOUT

DREARY NO-SCORE DRAW

SUPER SQUASH!

JETS 97 SAINTS 106!

SPECTATOR BEHAVIOUR

Most spectators are well behaved but a small number often cause problems in a variety of ways. Here are two examples.

● Comments;
● Fighting.

Comments
Spectators often shout abuse at a team, player or official during an activity. Sometimes spectator behaviour can be really appalling.

BATSMAN SUFFERS RACIST COMMENTS FROM RIVAL SUPPORTERS

OFFICIALS CONCERNED AT BOOING DURING GOAL KICKS

Recently, crowd trouble reared its ugly head after Rugby Union matches in Wales.

As the players trooped from the field the referee, Ken McCartney, was tripped and kicked by a supporter - another absurd incident of hooliganism. Following a similar incident at Neath last Wednesday, Welsh rugby stands on trial for more than just its performance on the field as it braces itself to topple this devastating New Zealand side.

🛑 THOUGHT SPOT
Why do spectators behave in this way?

TASK 2
List other sports which have similar types of problems.

Fighting
Football attracts large crowds. Sadly, some rival supporters fight each other before, during and after games.

🛑 THOUGHT SPOT
Could what happens during an activity encourage crowd trouble? Do some people go to activities aiming to cause trouble? What do you think?

In recent years, sports have adopted some or all of the following measures to help overcome the problems of bad spectator behaviour.

1. Alcohol has been banned in sports grounds.

2. Grounds have been improved to increase safety and comfort (perimeter fencing, better facilities, more seating, etc.).

3. Fans are often segregated.

4. There is increased policing.

5. Closed-circuit television surveillance has been introduced.

6. Certain groups of spectators have been banned, e.g. Luton Town FC had a membership scheme, from 1985 up until August 1991, which only allowed 'home' fans into their games.

🛑 THOUGHT SPOT
What are the effects of a membership scheme like that used by Luton Town FC on:
a) home fans?
b) visiting fans?
c) people who live near the ground?
d) the police?
e) the teams?
f) the club?

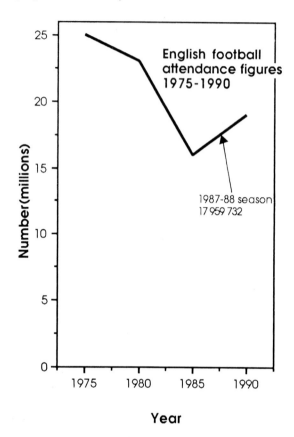

TASK 1

Study the graph below.

Can you suggest possible reasons why the graph has this shape?

English football attendance figures 1975-1990

1987-88 season
17 959 732

Number(millions)

25
20
15
10
5
0

1975   1980   1985   1990

Year

Crowd trouble

SUMMARY

Millions of people regularly watch sports and leisure pursuits on television or video. Many 'armchair' viewers may never attend live events.

Changes have been made to some activities in order to make them more 'watchable'.

Unruly **spectator behaviour** is a serious present-day problem.

Many attempts have been made, and are still being made, to eliminate unwanted spectator behaviour.

22

GEARED UP

Tennis in the 1940s

Tennis in the 1990s

Over the years, great changes have taken place in the special clothing, footwear and equipment needed in physical activities. There are three reasons behind the changes.

1. Safety

Many items have been designed to improve safety.

A modern, quick release binding holding a boot to a ski

2. Fashion

Sportswear is a growing part of the clothing industry and has become very fashionable. More and more attention is being paid to colour, fabric and design. Indeed, it is frequently worn away from the sports place as 'leisure wear'.

3. Performance

Better equipment design can lead to improved performance. Designers try to improve their products by:

a) reducing weight, e.g. a modern athletics shoe weighs only a few grams;

b) changing the shape or the size, e.g. a tennis mid-head racket;

c) reducing the resistance (friction) between two surfaces, e.g. ski wax;

d) increasing the resistance (friction) between two surfaces, e.g. different 'rubbers' on table-tennis bats produce different spins.

A bottle of wax for coating skis

TASK

Look at the items of clothing and equipment below. Can you list some of the changes which designers have made over the years? Use the information on page 23 to help you.

TASK 2

Investigate one activity. List the design changes which have led to improved performance in the last ten years.

2. The length of a golf club must be appropriate to the height of the player.

Equipment is designed to suit people of different ages, abilities and body shape. Here are two examples.

1. The length and weight of a tennis racket is important. A beginner or younger person is best suited to a racket which is shorter, lighter and has a narrower grip than the full-size model.

SUMMARY

Clothing, footwear and equipment have changed dramatically over the years, for three reasons:

- safety;
- fashion;
- to aid performance.

SAFETY IN PHYSICAL ACTIVITIES

Accidents happen in many activities. In most cases, they are the result of carelessness. Safety is important not only to the people taking part, but also to teachers, coaches, spectators and organisers.

SAFETY AND YOU

In order to do as well as you can in any activity, you must prepare *fully* beforehand. This means having:

● the necessary type of fitness;
● the necessary level of fitness;
● the ability to perform the skills needed;
● prepared thoroughly both physically and mentally (often known as 'the warm-up').

KIT AND EQUIPMENT

Every activity requires kit (clothes and foot-wear); some activities require equipment.

TASK 1

Choose an activity, and list all the kit and equipment needed by one performer. Say why each item is needed.

To reduce the risk of injury, it is essential to make sure all kit fits properly and is in good repair, and that all equipment is in good working order.

In some activities, special equipment is worn to protect different parts of the body. For example, a visor is worn by fencers to protect the face.

TASK 2

The photographs opposite show protective clothing and equipment. For each, name the activity, the safety item and the body part which is being protected.

SAFETY AND OTHERS

Physical contact is a feature of many activities, either by design or accident.

Other performers are affected by your behaviour. Whatever your activity, learn its rules or guidelines, and always perform within them.

You may be involved in group activities in which you have to give support, e.g. as a 'spotter'. Your partner or group must be confident that you can do this important job which involves:

● being strong enough to hold the performer;
● reacting quickly should a problem arise;
● concentrating fully.

Javelins being held correctly in a class

SAFETY AND RULES

The supervision of activities varies. Some activities are governed by rules: a referee, umpire or judge will ensure that the performers perform within the rules.

In others, there may be supervision or help available. However, you are expected to follow certain rules and instructions at all times.

You and your friends may do an activity without supervision, and must therefore follow a code of conduct.

SAFETY AND EQUIPMENT

There are three things to watch out for here.

1. The area in which the activity takes place can be potentially hazardous.

2. 'Light' equipment must always be handled and used correctly.

3. Equipment must always be set up correctly.

SUMMARY

Safety is an important consideration in every physical activity.
Many activities require protective clothing and equipment.
You have a responsibility to yourself, to your team mates and to your opponents to make sure your actions are *safe*.
Ability and level of fitness may affect safety considerations for any individual or group of individuals.
The type of activity, the facilities and the equipment used can all be dangerous unless rules and regulations are followed carefully.
The level of **supervision** depends on the activity and the level at which it is played.

SPORT AND DRUGS

OLYMPIC CHAMPION FOUND GUILTY OF TAKING DRUGS

As a result of drug testing Ben Johnson has been stripped of his gold medal and world record.

In many ways, the 1988 Seoul Olympics were a huge success:

● the facilities were superb;
● thousands of athletes from many countries competed;
● spectator attendances were very high;
● a number of records were set.

Sadly, the Games will also be remembered for the wrong reason—the drugs scandal. Ten athletes in a variety of events were found guilty of taking illegal drugs, and a number of athletes withdrew from competition when their fellow countrymen were found guilty (perhaps this indicated they too were taking drugs and could only avoid detection by withdrawing).

POSITIVE DRUG-TESTING AT THE OLYMPIC GAMES

The problem of drug taking has been around for many years.

Venue	Year	Positive Tests
Mexico	1968	1
Munich	1972	7
Montreal	1976	11
Moscow	1980	0
Los Angeles	1984	11
Seoul	1988	10

Testing has taken place in the Olympic Games since 1968, but drug taking has been with us since at least 1956. After retiring, Harold Connelly, the 1956 Olympic Hammer champion, admitted he had taken drugs in preparation for his event.

There are many different types of drug used in sport but they are taken for one reason only—to improve performance.

WHY DO PEOPLE TAKE DRUGS?

Sport at the highest level nowadays can bring fame and fortune to those who are successful. Ben Johnson may have lost as much as ten million dollars in the time he was banned from the sport.

The public and media thrive on success and want to see it. Pressure from these sources is always on the performer.

HOW DO DRUGS WORK?

The main drugs are anabolic steroids, stimulants, beta blockers and diuretics.

1. Anabolic steroids are most frequently used for two reasons: to increase muscle development and to allow athletes to train for longer periods. They were first used by athletes in field events.

🛈 THOUGHT SPOT

Do you know why?

2. Stimulants can help athletes withstand pain during training and also help them to train for longer periods.

3. Beta blockers help to calm the nerves and are used in activities where good control and concentration are important, e.g. snooker.

🛈 THOUGHT SPOT

Can you think of other examples?

4. Diuretics help reduce weight by removing water from the body. They are commonly found in events requiring strict weight control, e.g. boxing.

Blood doping, though not a drugs issue, is also an illegal practice. See Unit 27 for more information.

DRUGS AND HEALTH

The drugs mentioned earlier are often prescribed by doctors to patients. For example, after the Second World War people who had been prisoners of war were given steroids to help them put on weight.

However, if an athlete takes drugs to improve performance, he or she risks health problems including cancer, liver damage, weakened blood vessels, infertility and heart disease. Many deaths are believed to have occurred; the most well known perhaps being the West German heptathlete who received more than 400 injections in a year as she moved from thirty-third to sixth place in the world rankings. She died from toxic poisoning in 1988.

TASK 1

Find out who this was.

THE PROBLEM OF DETECTION

Drug detection can be a problem for the authorities in two ways.

1. If an athlete stops taking drugs in sufficient time before an event, no trace of the drug will be found.

2. Other drugs can be taken to prevent the illegal drug being detected. These are known as masking agents, and are illegal too. Many are found in common drugs available at the chemist. Athletes must therefore be careful about what medication they take—even the simple cough cure contains banned substances.

THE FUTURE

The Sports Council has recently announced that three drug-testing centres will be set up in Britain. A drugs helpline will also be operated to offer advice to young athletes.

🛈 THOUGHT SPOT

1. What can be done to prevent the spread of drugs in sport?
2. What would you do if an athlete had a positive drugs test, and
   a) you were organising the event?
   b) you were a fellow competitor who did not take drugs?
   c) you were a businessman sponsoring the athlete?

Ben Johnson was found guilty of taking illegal drugs to improve his performance. Coaches, doctors and other athletes were also found to have been involved. Drug testing procedures have been improved. Athletes will now be subjected to random drug testing in training and in competition.

Will drug taking simply continue, with athletes unconcerned about the effects trying to outwit those in charge by looking for new drugs which are perhaps harder to detect or, as yet, unbanned?

INFO BOX

In 1988, Tour de France champion Pedro Dalgado was found to have used 'Prebenicid'. Although banned for athletes, it was not yet banned for cyclists and so he was not disqualified.

The Sports Council and Scottish Sports Council have announced a new system of drug testing in many sports. Young athletes and performers may also be tested. Testing will be more frequent. Willie Anderson, the Irish rugby international, is the first rugby player to have been found taking a banned substance.

THOUGHT SPOT
1. What effect will the Ben Johnson case have on sport, especially athletics?
2. Will competitors clean up their act or will they attempt to outwit the authorities? If so, why?
3. Are authorities and governing bodies really doing enough to combat the problem? Could the testing systems be improved?
4. Should school-aged children be the subject of random drug testing?

SUMMARY

The use of **drugs** in sport is an increasing problem today.

The benefits in terms of fame, status, privilege and money which result from success can motivate performers to take illegal drugs.

Drugs are taken for different purposes but all will help performance.

Different drugs have different effects on the body. Those mentioned in this unit are taken for one purpose—to improve performance.

The detection of drugs is becoming more difficult as athletes find ways to avoid being caught.

SPORT AND POLITICS

Zola Budd

It seems as if sport throughout the world is continually being influenced, if not controlled, by politicians. Sometimes their involvement is welcome, but history shows that many sporting occasions have been affected by political issues.

Competing at international level, whatever the sport, is certainly important for the team or individuals involved. The result of international competition, however, can be of interest to a whole nation.

 THOUGHT SPOT

How do you feel when you see a team or individual from your country doing very well or very badly?

How much importance should be placed on winning?

For some nations success is all important. Many Eastern European countries and Third World countries would argue that winning at international level shows that their lifestyle and attitude to sport is the best. In such countries sport is often financed and controlled by the state with facilities, equipment and coaching all provided and paid for by the state to help performers reach the top in their sport.

A different attitude is found in many Western European countries and the USA. Historically, national associations, independent of government, have been responsible for the administration and development of sport. Gradually governments have played a bigger role, by providing finance and support, as the need for facilities and coaching has grown. Britain, for example, has a Sports Council set up and funded by the Government which helps the administration and development of sport at local and national level. (See Unit 4 for further information.)

Increased involvement of governments has also brought with it a bigger say for politicians in decisions affecting teams and individuals, both amateur and professional. Many amateur performers feel that representing their country is the highest honour available and that this opportunity should not be denied to them for political reasons. Some professionals argue that, as their chosen activity is their way of earning a living, it should be up to them to decide where and against whom they can compete.

 THOUGHT SPOT

What part do you think a government should play in sport?

Success in international competition can have benefits for the individual, team or nation, but the desire to win can become too strong and result in rule breaking. Alternatively, pressure from others may have the same effect and result in cheating. In addition, spectators may react badly at times of defeat.

 THOUGHT SPOT

How important should sport be to an individual or a nation?

Many sporting events have been boycotted or disrupted by politics, but to understand how and why, it is necessary to know about the political issues.

POLITICAL ISSUES AFFECTING SPORT

According to the founder of the Olympic Games, Pierre de Coubertin, the Olympics were to bring more peace and understanding between nations. However, many Olympic Games have been affected by political influences.

If a country treats either some of its own people or another country badly, this can result in criticism from others. The Soviet Union has often been accused, on the issue of human rights, for its severe treatment of some individuals and minority groups. As a result of this and its military occupation of Afghanistan, many western countries, including the USA, boycotted the 1980 Olympics held in Moscow.

Conflict between nations has caused problems for Israel with her Arab neighbours. Israel is founded on land once known as Palestine and is not recognised as a nation by most Arab countries. As a result, most of these countries refuse to take part in international competition with Israel.

Sport has also been used as a way of drawing the attention of a world audience. Hitler used the 1936 Olympics in Berlin to try to persuade the world of the superiority of the German nation.

Apartheid, however, is perhaps the biggest human rights issue and can cause problems throughout the sporting world. South Africa, although dominated by black people, is ruled by a white minority. The government's policy has been to separate the different racial groups—a policy known as apartheid. This policy resulted in discrimination against non-whites in sport. Facilities and opportunities have been inferior for non-whites, and spectators are often segregated. An all-white South African team was chosen to represent them in the 1960 Olympics, only to have its invitation withdrawn. In 1970, South Africa was expelled from the Olympic movement.

Many countries then took steps to break all links with South Africa, and in 1977 countries in the Commonwealth signed a declaration, called the Gleneagles Agreement, which banned all sporting links with South Africa. However, not every-one has kept to the agreement. Some teams and individuals have ignored advice from their government and played in South Africa. When this happens, member countries of the Gleneagles Agreement can act in three ways:

- boycotting an event if it is to include a player or team with South African links;
- denying access or entry to a player or team with South African links;
- refusing to select a player with South African links for his or her own international team.

THE FUTURE

The 1990s may bring some dramatic changes of government in some countries, especially in Eastern Europe, which in time may affect attitudes to sport. For example, East and West Germany have undergone a process of reunification which has seen sporting teams combine. One effect of this may be an even more powerful force in world sport. On the other hand, training methods and coaching ideas from East Germany, admired and envied by many, may now be shared by the rest of the world.

In South Africa too, change is happening. Whites and non-whites are talking about sharing power, and one day we may see South Africa return to the international stage with multi-racial teams.

SUMMARY

Not all countries have the same attitudes to sport. Although most governments take an interest in the development of sport, the control that politicians have over sport depends on the organisation of sport in that country.
Some countries, especially in Eastern Europe, have seen success in sport as all important, but a change in attitude may soon happen as a result of changes in government.
The involvement of politicians in sport can have benefits, but history also shows that many international sporting occasions have been disrupted as a result of political events.

HOW SKILFUL ARE YOU?

A **physical skill** is a movement or a number of linked movements performed with a definite *purpose* (e.g. passing—to play the ball to a team-mate).

TASK 1

Attempt each of the following skills and gauge how well you do. Your marks will range from 10 (skilful) to 1 (not skilful). If you are unable to perform any of the skills, give yourself a score based on how well you think you would do.

1. Walk 10 metres in a straight line.
2. Throw a tennis ball with your 'good' hand to a partner or target 20 metres away.
3. Perform skill 2 again except throw the ball with your other hand.
4. Do a 360° jump turn without losing your balance. (i.e. Stand on one spot, jump into the air, turn round once to land on the same spot.)
5. Throw a tennis ball or bean-bag into the air, just above your head, and 'catch' it using only your foot.
6. Perform a forward roll without using your hands to help you up to your feet.
7. Balance on one leg for 30 seconds.
8. Swim 20 metres using the butterfly stroke.
9. Carry out a dance sequence involving different movements for at least 20 seconds.
10. Kick a rugby ball and make it spin like a torpedo.

You will probably have found some of these skills easier to perform than others.

INFO BOX

You are more skilful in some skills because:
a) they maybe simple, i.e. they only involve a few easy movements joined together; or
b) you have been taught the skill before and have learned to be skilful; or
c) very few judgements (decisions) have to be made.

You are less skilful in other skills because:
a) they may be complex, i.e. they involve a number of difficult movements which link together in exactly the right order and with correct timing; or
b) you have never had an opportunity to perform the skill before, or been taught it; or
c) the skill involves a number of complex judgements.

HOW DO WE RECOGNISE A SKILFUL PERFORMER?

Here are some things to look for in a skilful performer.

1. Effectiveness—this is the ability to achieve the purpose of the skill.

2. Judgement—this is the ability to make correct decisions in response to what is going on around the performer, and *may* include:
a) **skill selection**—being able to choose the skill most likely to succeed;
b) **speed of skill selection**—making that selection as quickly as possible;
c) **timing**—judging exactly the right moment to begin the selected skill;
d) **creativity**—choosing to perform a skill which is unexpected by the opponent or the audience.

3. Co-ordination—this is the ability to link movements into a flowing action, through the correct positions, with the correct 'weight'.

4. Reaction time—this is the time it takes for a stimulus such as sight, touch, hearing, to reach your brain and for a message to be sent back to the muscles to allow the skill to be performed.

The table below shows what is needed to be a skilful performer in four different types of activity. (Note: ✓ = important to skill × = not important to skill.)

TASK 2

Choose three other activities from the following list and decide which 'things to look for' are important to be a skilful performer.

Dance; Sprinting; Croquet; Lacrosse; Judo; Sailing; Ski-jumping.

INFO BOX

Some skills are said to be 'closed' and others 'open'. A **closed skill** involves the same action being repeated for every performance, for example in the high jump, swimming or archery. Very little decision-making takes place in closed skills.

An **open skill** is different from a closed skill because it relies upon you deciding *which* skill to use in response to what you see going on around you, and then deciding *when* and *how* to perform it. Open skills are not always performed in the same way every time, for example in a tennis volley the ball will hardly ever come towards you the same way. This means that slight changes in the way you perform the skill will always have to be made depending on how you see the ball.

Things to look for	Tennis	Golf	Javelin	Diving
Effectiveness	✓	✓	✓	✓
Skill selection	✓	✓	×	✓
Speed of skill selection	✓	×	×	×
Timing	✓	✓	✓	✓
Creativity	✓	✓	×	✓
Coordination	✓	✓	✓	✓
Reaction time	✓	×	×	×

← CLOSED SKILLS   OPEN SKILLS →

On the line above, closed skills are shown at one end and open skills at the other. Archery is a closed skill because the actions in the skill are always the same. In the climbing example, the mountaineers are having to decide which skill is best depending on the features of the rockface.

TASK 3

Place the following skills on the line:
a) cricket stroke;
b) gymnastic vault;
c) drop shot in badminton;
d) side step in rugby;
e) javelin throwing;
f) basketball free throw.

🛈 THOUGHT SPOT

It is possible for some closed skills to be performed in an 'open' situation. For example, a tennis stroke can be practised as a closed skill but used in a game as an open skill when the time is right.

SUMMARY

A physical skill is a movement or a number of linked movements performed with a definite *purpose*.

Depending on the activity or the skill a skilful performer may require:

● **judgement**;
● **co-ordination**;
● **creativity**.

A skilful performer must be **effective**, i.e. the purpose of the skill must be achieved.

'**Closed**' skills require the performer to follow a series of movements which are identical on every occasion, giving the same action every time.

'**Open**' skills require the performer to decide which skill to perform depending on what he or she sees. Open skills are not always performed the same way every time.

Note: see Units 15 and 16 for further information about skills and how we can improve them.

TECHNIQUE AND STYLE

In Unit 11, we said that a physical skill was a movement or a number of linked movements performed with a definite purpose. The table below shows some examples of skills used in certain activities.

Activity	Skill	Purpose
A Hockey	Shooting	To score
B Athletics	Jumping	To jump as high as possible
C Skiing	Turning	To change direction

We use the word **technique** to describe a recognised way of performing a skill. Here are examples of techniques used to perform the skills in the above table.

A Hockey
 Skill: shooting
 Technique 1: the flick
 Technique 2: the hit

The flick

The hit

B Athletics
Skill: jumping
Technique 1: the Fosbury flop
Technique 2: the straddle

The
Fosbury
flop

The
Straddle

C Skiing
Skill: turning
Technique 1: parallel turn
Technique 2: snowplough turn

Parallel
turn

Snowplough
turn

BREAKING DOWN TECHNIQUES

In some activities, it is possible to practise part of a technique on its own in order to improve the whole technique.
Here are some examples

This player might practise only the jump.

Skill: attacking shot
Technique: spike or dump

The
Spike

This gymnast might practise landing from a height onto two feet.

Skill: vault
Technique: cartwheel quarter turn

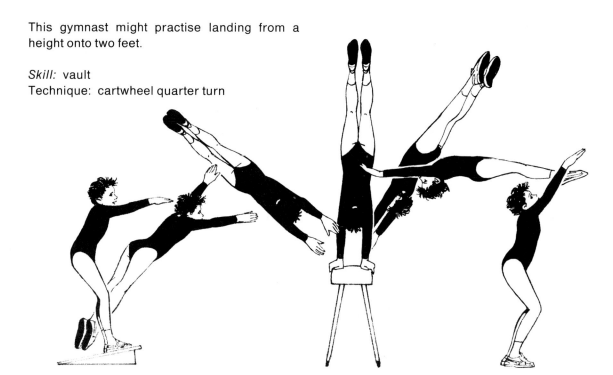

This swimmer might hold a float in her hands and only work on improving her leg action.

Skill: swimming
Technique: front crawl

STYLISH PERFORMERS

A stylish performer can link all the different parts of a technique into one smooth flowing action—he or she performs with style, showing 'good form'. There are, however, many stylish performers who are not effective, i.e. they do not achieve the purpose of certain skills. Reasons for not being effective include:

● lack of concentration;
● lack of confidence;
● physical size;
● lack of power.

There are also performers who do not follow the normal technique but who still perform the skill successfully!

🛈 THOUGHT SPOT
A technique suitable for one person may not be suitable for another because of physical size or preference.
Can you think of examples?

SUMMARY

Technique describes a recognised way of performing a skill.
Style describes how the technique is performed. If a performer follows the technique correctly, he or she can be said to have shown 'good form'.
Skilful performers may not follow the normal technique but may still be successful.
Stylish performers are not always successful; this may be a result of lack of concentration, lack of confidence, physical size or lack of power.

UNIT 13 EXPRESSIVE MOVEMENT

TASK 1

Touch four words below which you think could describe how each performer in the photographs is showing emotion. The words describe movement 'qualities'.

strong high light smooth powerful

jerky **soft** heavy fast *angled*

stiff *quick* tight **slow** jagged low

All of the performers in the photographs are showing (expressing) a different feeling or an emotion by moving in different ways. This illustrates how we can express emotions through our bodies.

Each emotion shown in the photographs is a **response** to something that has happened, and is really felt by the performer.

However, we can show emotions to other people without having to feel the emotion ourselves. We do this by imagining different emotions and then expressing these to other people using our bodies.

- Our body can 'speak' for us.
- Other people 'listen' to what we are saying by watching and feeling the emotions we express.

The movements of the ice-skaters have been planned in advance and linked to music (choreographed). Depending on which emotion they wish to express, they will give the movements they perform different qualities. These qualities can be placed under four headings:

- **Time**, e.g. quick;
- **Weight**, e.g. heavy;
- **Space**, e.g. wide;
- **Flow**, e.g. smooth.

TASK 2

Using the list of qualities given at the beginning of this unit, put each one under one of these headings.

Dancers use combinations of time, weight, space and flow in a very deliberate way to *convey* (put across) an emotion to an audience who may feel the emotion for themselves.

SUMMARY

We can express emotions (show feelings) using only our body movements.
We can imagine these emotions and then convey them to others by using our bodies.
We can place body movements under four headings: Time, Weight, Space and Flow.

MAY THE FORCE BE WITH YOU

All physical skills involve **forces** (pushes and pulls). Knowledge of forces can help us understand why techniques have been developed. The diagrams on this page show how forces act to create **motion**.

The force from the volleyball player's legs is greater than the force of gravity, so he can jump into the air.

The force from the swimmer's legs and arms overcomes the opposite forces of drag or resistance of the water, so she swims forward.

In addition, the streamlined body position cuts down the effect of **drag**, and the upward force of **buoyancy** works against the force of **gravity** to keep the swimmer afloat.

All forces have direction. If the force going one way is greater than the force going the other, then **motion** takes place in the direction of the stronger force.

Here, the forces of each set of rugby forwards are equal. They cancel each other out; there is no movement.

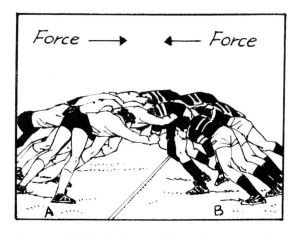

However, if the B players' force is greater than that of the A players, then motion happens in the direction of the arrow.

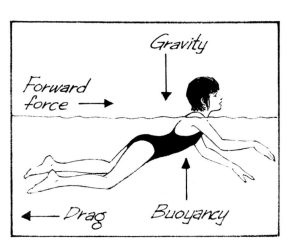

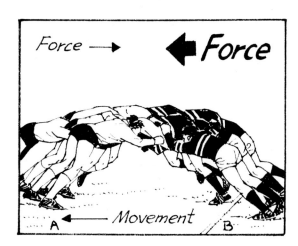

Look at the two diagrams below. Explain why the performers have taken up those body positions.

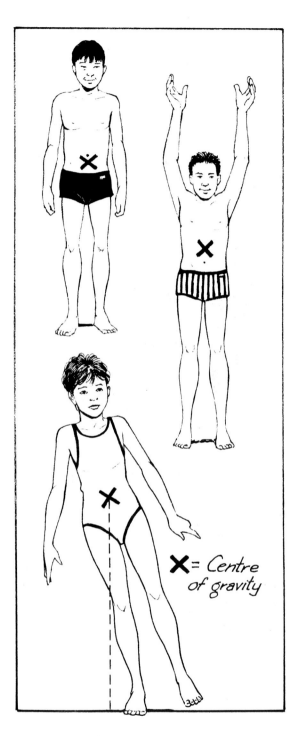

✗ = *Centre of gravity*

THE CENTRE OF GRAVITY

In many activities **balance** can be very important. Gravity plays an important part in balance. Gravity is a force pulling an object or person to the ground.

The point at which gravity acts on the body is known as the **centre of gravity**. This will change depending on your height, shape or the position in which you stand. For example if you stand up straight your centre of gravity (marked *x* in the diagrams) is said to be in a position just below the navel, but raising your arms above your head or moving them to one side will change its position.

Balance is not difficult while a person's centre of gravity is directly above their 'base', but when it moves to one side, the force of gravity will act more on that side causing the person to topple over.

Follow the instructions in the following tasks exactly.

TASK **2**

1. Press the right-hand side of your body against a wall, i.e. your right foot, leg, hip, arm and shoulder.
2. Lift your left leg off the ground.
   What happens?
   Why does this happen?

TASK **3**

1. Stand (away from the wall) with your feet about shoulder-width apart.
2. Lift your left leg off the ground—do not fall over.
   What did you do with your body that stopped you from falling over?

The above tasks might not seem related to physical activities, but if you did them properly you should now realise the importance of a person's centre of gravity (CoG). Balance depends on keeping the centre of gravity above the area of the base. Whether standing still or moving, correct balance is very important in physical activities.

TASK **4**

Perform the following skills:
  a) walking;
  b) playing a golf shot, a hockey hit and a cricket stroke;
  c) throwing a shot putt;
  d) throwing a basketball chest pass.

Did your centre of gravity have to move to maintain balance during the skills?

TASK **5**

Using your knowledge about centre of gravity, list three techniques which depend on allowing the centre of gravity to go outside the area of the base in order to perform the skill, e.g. the technique of cartwheeling.

TASK **6**

Find magazine or newspaper photographs of different activities where each performer has one or more of the following features:
  a) a wide base;
  b) a low centre of gravity;
  c) a centre of gravity within the area of the base.

What effect do these features have on the skill?

INFO BOX

Stability depends on:

- keeping the centre of gravity within the area of the base;
- the area of base;
- the height of the centre of gravity.

The more stable you are the easier it is to change direction or move quickly from a stationary position.

SUMMARY

Forces are 'pushes' and 'pulls'.

Motion will take place in the direction of the strongest 'push' or 'pull'.

Techniques are developed in response to these forces (e.g. hammer throwing and skiing).

The centre of gravity in a body is the point through which all the force of gravity pulls down.

Balance can only be maintained if the centre of gravity is kept within the area of the base (unless there are other forces acting).

The lower the centre of gravity, the more stable an object or person will be, since it will be easier to keep the centre of gravity within the area of the base.

The more stable you are, the easier it is to change direction or move quickly from a stationary position.

Wide base

Centre of gravity within area of base

Low centre of gravity

IT'S ALL IN THE MIND

" I felt so good I knew
I couldn't lose"

" I was so relaxed it was easy"

" I lost concentration
as I putted"

" I got so excited I could not think"

" I felt really uptight
before the race"

MENTAL PREPARATION

Here are two examples of mental preparation.

These statements were all made by sports
people after taking part in competition.

TASK 1

Read the statements again, and decide which
were made by winners, and which were made
by losers.

In this unit, we will explore how success in sport
is affected by the **mind**.
All performers need **motivation**—a reason for
taking part in an activity.
Motivation is the driving force behind performance. Good performers tend to be very highly
motivated.

In the lead-up to an event, many performers
spend most of their time preparing their
bodies—this is **physical preparation**. Little time,
however, is spent on preparing their minds—
this is **mental preparation**.

These show two completely different types of
mental preparation for sport. (Notice the different types of sport.) In the first picture, the athlete
has closed her eyes, is relaxing and thinking
only about the coming race (concentration of the
highest level). As she relaxes, she pictures the
whole race in her mind (from start to finish) to
help her performance—this is called **mental
rehearsal**. In the second picture, the American
footballer is being shouted at by his coach. As
the shouting and yelling by the coach (and probably his team-mates, too) continues, he
becomes more and more excited in readiness
for going onto the field to take part in a very
physical game.

❗ THOUGHT SPOT

What might happen to the sprinter if she were to prepare like the American footballer?

TASK 2

Do you mentally prepare before your favourite activity? If so, how?

Choose an activity other than athletics and American football, and find out all you can about the mental preparation involved.

Concentration is the ability to keep your attention on what you are doing (to prevent your mind from wandering). It is an important factor in good performance.

TASK 3

1. Find an example where good concentration has led to a successful performance.
2. Find an example where a performance has been spoiled by poor concentration.

Note: these examples may be found in newspapers, magazines, sports books, etc.

TASK 4

Investigate the effect of motivation on performance (e.g. class cheering and urging a performer to greater effort). Chart the results and look for trends. Check with your teacher that your plan is safe before carrying it out.

PERSONALITY

Someone who is active, independent, carefree, talkative and lively is often described as **extrovert**. Someone who has an **introvert** personality is likely to be quiet, calm, shy, reserved and careful.

❗ THOUGHT SPOT

Think of people you know and decide if they are introvert or extrovert.

In general, extroverts and introverts usually prefer different activities from one another. Extroverts prefer team games involving others. Introverts prefer individual activities where they can rely on themselves.

TASK 5

Study the list of activities below. Which of them might suit an extrovert, and which might suit an introvert?

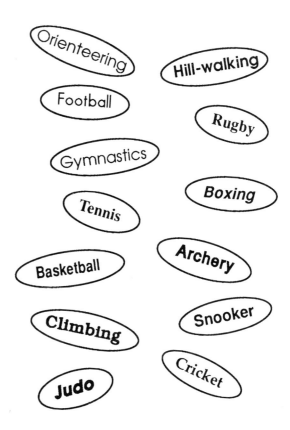

Orienteering · Hill-walking · Football · Rugby · Gymnastics · Boxing · Tennis · Archery · Basketball · Snooker · Climbing · Cricket · Judo

INFO BOX

Success in sport depends on many factors—one of them is how well an individual handles **stress**. All the things which can mentally affect your performance add up to give stress, for example having to be successful all the time, fear of failure, large crowds, prize money.

SUMMARY

Mental preparation is of great importance to performance, yet it is often neglected.
Concentration helps performance.
People with different personalities often prefer different types of activity.
Motivation is the driving force behind performance.
Motivation affects the level of performance.

PRACTICE MAKES PERFECT

THOUGHT SPOT

What do you think the golfer meant when he said that practice made him luckier?

Think of a baby learning to walk and then think of yourself walking: what are the obvious differences between the two? Do they include the fact that the baby often falls whilst you don't, and that the baby is unsteady whilst you are not? A major difference is the fact that you perform the skill of walking **automatically** (without thinking) whilst the baby does not. The baby is still learning.

THOUGHT SPOT

Why are you often asked to repeat a skill over and over again when learning it for the first time?

HOW DO WE PERFORM SKILLS?

To perform actions in the proper order, with correct timing and 'weighting' requires **co-ordination**. Consider the skill of catching a ball.

Stage 1 You *see* the ball.
Stage 2 You *judge* the speed, distance, height and direction of the ball.
Stage 3 You predict the final position of the ball and move your hands accordingly.
Stage 4 You close your hands around the ball, with the correct 'weight', making the catch.

These four stages depend on the coordination of your eyes and hands, linked by the **sensory nerves (neurones)**, the **brain**, **motor nerves (neurones)** and **muscles** (in the arms and the hands), i.e. the **sensory pathway** (see Unit 21). The more practice you have at catching, the smoother and more coordinated your catch will become. You learn the sensory pathway for that skill.

When catching a ball, the sense of sight picks up messages which are sent to the brain. There are other **senses** which we can use to gather information when taking part in activities.

1. Touch

The climber **feels** for a hand-hold before moving upwards.

2. Hearing

The athlete depends on the sense of **hearing** in order to hear the starter's gun.

3. Internal kinaesthetic sense

The diver is using what is called his **internal kinaesthetic sense**. This allows him to judge the *position* of his body through messages sent back to the brain from the **muscles**, **tendons** and **joints**.

❗ THOUGHT SPOT

Can you name three sports where kinaesthetic sense is vitally important?

Work with a partner through the following tasks.

TASK 1

Tell your partner to close his/her eyes, and then with one finger to touch his/her nose, knee, toes and other finger tips.

TASK 2

Ask your partner to throw a tennis ball to you while you hit it back with a racket. *Keep your eyes on the ball all the time.* How do you know what the racket is doing?

Tell your partner to *close his/her eyes*, sit down on the floor with legs spread out, straighten legs and point toes, raise head, lift up arms at sides, straighten arms, hands and fingers, tense all muscles.

Remember to change roles and have a go yourself.

TASK CHECK

1. Kinaesthetic sense allowed you to know the position and movement of your finger.
2. Kinaesthetic sense allowed you to be aware of the position of the racket.
3. Kinaesthetic sense allowed you to feel the **tension** of the position and to judge how well you held it. If you consider the diver again, his kinaesthetic sense was his only way of knowing if his body was in the correct position.

INFO BOX

How your sense of balance works.

Very sensitive parts of your inner ear are constantly sending messages to your brain—and the brain responds by sending messages to your muscles which work together to stop you falling over.

FEEDBACK

The golfer on page 46 suggested that practice made him luckier. He was of course making a joke, as we now know that practice allows a skill to become more coordinated and successful.

The golfer improves his putting by repeating the skill again and again. As he practises he has three ways of *knowing* if he is successful. This is called **feedback**, as information is fed back to the performer.

1. He sees where the ball goes—**visual** feedback.
2. He feels what the skill is like—**kinaesthetic** feedback.
3. Less importantly, he hears the club hitting the ball—**sound** feedback.

Using the first two types of feedback, he can alter the skill to become more successful:

● with visual feedback he can aim the ball in a different direction;
● with kinaesthetic feedback he can strike the ball with a different force.

SUMMARY

Practice allows movements to become **automatic** (performed without thinking).

Coordination of nerves and muscles allows movements to take place in the correct order, and with the correct timing and weighting.

As a **skill** is practised, we learn the **sensory pathway**.

We gather information through all our senses of sight, hearing, touch, kinaesthesis and balance. Messages are sent to and from the brain which help us to perform skills.

Feedback of various kinds lets us know how well we have performed a skill.

TACTICS

> **Tactics:** *a system of play; making the best of your strengths, skills and abilities; exploiting weaknesses in the opposition.*

Performers often plan in advance how they will either play a game or approach an event or competition.

SMITH RUNS GOOD TACTICAL RACE

In many games and activities, 'tactics' are an important part of any good preparation. Before deciding which tactics to use, a number of factors must be considered. Let's look at two of them.

TEAM'S TACTICS PROVE SUCCESSFUL

1. The opposition

	Examples	
Considerations	Team	Individual
Style of play	Good at counter-attack	Adventurous, takes chances
Strengths	Good tacklers	Good forehand stroke
Weaknesses	Inexperienced goalkeeper	Poor backhand

By considering the opposition and themselves, performers can work out how to:
a) make the most of their own strengths;
b) cover up their own weaknesses;
c) expose, or play on, the opposition's weaknesses;
d) reduce the effectiveness of the opposition's strengths.

2. Playing conditions

The playing conditions may also be a consideration in planning tactics. Different conditions exist at different stages of a season and in different parts of the world. Here are two examples:
a) **surface**, e.g. hard, heavy, muddy, grass;
b) **weather**, e.g. dry, wet, windy, cold.

Good teams and individuals can alter their style of play to suit the conditions.

Tactics may be the responsibility of an individual, team captain or coach. A coach may often decide tactics in advance, with a captain or individual who has the responsibility to see that they are carried out during the activity. Tactics can be changed during play, either by the captain (on the field), or by the coach (off the field)—messages can be sent by signals from the dug-out or side line. Tactics can also be changed at recognised stoppages.

❗ THOUGHT SPOT

Think of activities where the following types of stoppage allow tactics to be changed: time-out; half-time; substitution.

Tactics may include:
a) creating space;
b) putting the opposition under pressure;
c) attacking areas of weakness in the opposition;
d) deceiving the opposition (pretending to do one thing and then doing another);
e) taking risks;
f) playing safe.

TASK 1

Describe two combinations of tactics you would suggest in the following circumstances if you were asked for advice about tactics.
a) A team game where the opposition is inexperienced but has a high level of fitness.
b) An individual game where the opposition is considered under pressure but has no real weaknesses.
c) A team game where your own side has a low skill but a high fitness level, while the opposition has a low level of fitness.

THE USE OF TACTICS

In high jump competitions, athletes are able to decide at which height they begin competing.

❗ THOUGHT SPOT

What advantages are there in entering a competition at a later stage (and therefore at a greater height) than the other competitors?

Timely substitution changes game and wins UEFA Cup for Barcelona

'Johann Cruyff, manager of Barcelona, brought on Rijkaard in the second half, and within minutes he scored the second goal to seal the 2-0 victory.'

TASK 2

Discuss whether this was a great tactical decision by Johann Cruyff or just good luck.

Scotland v France

'Scotland kicked off and the ball landed in touch. Instead of returning to the centre for a scrum as most teams do, the French took a quick lineout on the halfway line and ran in a try. Afterwards, it was revealed that this was a planned tactic by the French which had worked well.'

❗ THOUGHT SPOT

Superb opportunism or good tactics? What do you think?

SUMMARY

Tactics are an important part of any good preparation.
The opposition, yourself and the playing conditions must all be considered.
Tactical changes take place during play and at recognised stoppages.

COACHING AND LEARNING

UNIT 18

A coach can help a performer in two main ways:

a) by introducing new skills;
b) by helping the performer improve his/her skills.

In this unit, we will look at how the coach helps the performer in these ways.

INTRODUCING SKILLS TO A BEGINNER

First of all, the coach introduces the skill by explanation and demonstration. He or she can do this by performing the skill herself, making use of another performer, or showing a video or diagrams. In some skills it is possible for the performers to **imitate** or copy the demonstration.

Some difficult or complex skills have many different movements. If the performer has difficulty understanding everything that is involved, the coach can break the whole skill down into parts, and teach each of the parts separately.

Here is an example using the front crawl in swimming.

Firstly, the coach can introduce the leg kick to the performer. While the swimmer concentrates on his leg kick, he holds a float—so that he doesn't have to worry about his arms.

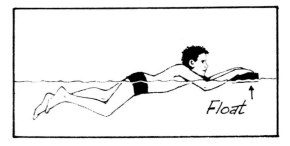

Once the coach thinks that the swimmer has mastered the kick, he or she introduces the arm action. A leg-float is held between the thighs— this allows the swimmer to concentrate on what his arms are doing.

Once the coach thinks that the swimmer has mastered the arm action, he or she asks the swimmer to put both parts together, and swim the complete front crawl.

HELPING THE PERFORMER IMPROVE SKILLS

Helping a performer to improve a skill is a natural development of introducing a new skill. The coach has three ways of doing this.

1. He or she can use the methods mentioned in introducing a new skill, i.e. explanation and demonstration, and breaking down the skill into parts. In addition to the latter, a coach can use a method of skill improvement known as **whole-part-whole**. In this method the coach asks the performer to repeat the whole skill, whilst closely observing the performance. Once a fault has been spotted, he or she designs a practice where the fault is worked on, and then asks the performer to practise the part of the skill which is causing problems. With the fault corrected, the coach asks the performer to try the whole skill—the performance should now be better.

2. Another and perhaps more important way in which the coach helps the performer is by **observing** (watching) and giving **feedback** (information about performance).

Observation is a very difficult skill, but one which you can learn. The important aspect of observation is being able to analyse the quality of the movements.

Feedback is important to performers, because it is often very difficult for them to know if they are performing a skill correctly. By giving feedback, the coach can let the performer know if he/she is doing a skill properly (**positive feedback**), or can explain what to do to make a skill better (**corrective feedback**). It would be 'bad' coaching to only tell a performer he/she is doing something wrong, without saying how to improve it.

3. A third way the coach can help a performer to improve skills is to make him/her practise (try out) the skills in progressively more demanding situations. For example, hockey players learning how to improve their dribbling skills might be asked by the coach to practise in the following situations:

a) free dribbling, going in any direction, walking;
b) free dribbling, going in any direction, running;
c) free dribbling, changing direction as told;
d) dribbling around cones;
e) dribbling around a defender who provides 'passive' opposition;
f) dribbling around a defender who provides 'active' opposition;
g) dribbling in a small-sided game, e.g. 2 v 1;
h) dribbling in progressively larger-sided games, e.g. 3 v 2, 3 v 3, 5 v 3, 5 v 5.
i) full game.

The coach designs a session where initially the performer is under little or no pressure. As the performer becomes more competent, the pressure can be increased.

TASK
Think of two very different physical activities where skills can be developed in simple situations, and later transferred to the full activity. Try to think of at least five stages.

TASK 1
Work with a partner. Choose a skill you both know well. Imagine you are a coach and your partner is a performer. Observe your partner's performance, and offer positive or corrective feedback.

SUMMARY

A coach can introduce new skills to a performer.
The parts of a **complex skill** can be taught and practised separately.
A coach can also help a performer improve skills.
The **whole-part-whole** method is a common method of skills teaching.
Feedback is of vital importance to the performer.
Practice situations can be made progressively more difficult.

SIZE AND SHAPE

In some activities, being a certain shape or size can be important. For example, basketball tends to be dominated by tall players, whilst jockeys tend to be small, light and muscular.

🛈 THOUGHT SPOT
Can you think why?

One method of describing body shapes is called **somatotyping**. It was developed by an American called Sheldon. He believed that three kinds of body type could be identified.

- **Endomorph**—pear-shaped body, wide hips and narrow shoulders with a large amount of body fat.
- **Mesomorph**—wide at the shoulders, narrow hips, strong muscular arms and legs.
- **Ectomorph**—thin body, narrow at the shoulders, long thin arms and legs, little muscle or body fat.

TASK 1
Can you match each description with one of the pictures above?

Sheldon really only saw these shapes as extremes, with an individual having varying degrees of all three. He had a test which involved taking various measurements, including the thickness of body fat. Each individual was given a score for each body type on a scale of 1 to 7. For example, a rating of 5,3,2, means high endomorphy (5), low mesomorphy (3), and low ectomorphy (2).

TASK 2
Your teacher may be able to assess you according to Sheldon's methods. If not, work with a partner to gather the following information about yourself.

> Height;
> Weight;
> Length of arm;
> Length of upper leg;
> Centre of gravity in relation to height.

(See Unit 14 for an explanation of centre of gravity.)

Participants in some activities can be a variety of shapes and sizes, for example the players in a Rugby Union team.

Size or shape can help in a number of ways in some activities.

The length of a boxer's arm (his reach) can be very important!

If staying upright is important, then being small may help.

For example, a gymnast cartwheeling on the beam

WEIGHT AND STRENGTH

Shot-putting and sprinting are both 'power' events which require strength and speed. However, two people of the same weight and size may not be as powerful as each other.

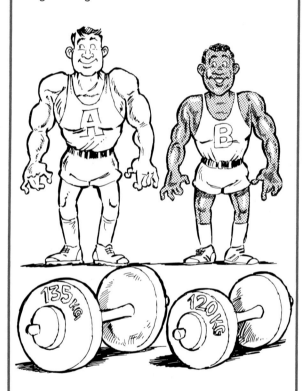

Weight is used to group competitors in certain activities, for example boxing.

TASK 3

Find out about this activity, and re-arrange this list in the correct order, from lightest to heaviest.

Light weight	Light-welter weight
Middle weight	Fly weight
Light-fly weight	Light-middle weight
Light-heavy weight	Heavy weight
Super-heavy weight	Feather weight
Bantam weight	

THOUGHT SPOT

Which other activities have weight divisions? Which activity has a 'penalty system' involving weights?

CHANGING THE RULES

Your size or shape can often be an advantage or disadvantage, but do not let it put you off an activity. You might lack a few inches in height or bulging muscles but you can make up for it in other ways. You may also find that the rules of some activities have been changed in your favour. Basketball is a good example.

Basketball is often seen as a game suited only to very tall players, and in the early days of the sport this was certainly the case. Tall players found it easy to score, and as a result a restricted area around the basket was introduced. Nowadays, attacking players are only allowed in the zone for three seconds at a time. In 1984 another line was drawn and players scoring from outside are awarded three points instead of the usual two. Smaller, faster players who are able to dribble, pass and shoot accurately play a vital part in today's game.

As well as size and shape, the age of the performers may be taken into account by the organisers of an activity. For example:

a) the area of play may be reduced, e.g. trim volleyball (four-a-side) is played on a badminton court;

b) the height of the net may be adjusted, e.g. the mini-basket net is eight feet from the floor while for full basketball it is ten feet from the floor;

c) special equipment may be used, e.g. short tennis, used to introduce tennis technique, is played with light and short rackets;

d) the numbers in a team may be adjusted, e.g. many activities have mini or midi versions for youngsters;

e) the time a game is played for may be reduced.

THOUGHT SPOT

Can you think of any other examples where the rules of an activity are changed to take account of the size, shape or age of the performers?

SUMMARY

We all look different, but basically there are three main body shapes.

Size or **shape** can be an advantage in certain activities.

Some activities may group people for competition according to shape or size.

The rules of an activity may be changed to take account of the size, shape, or age of the performers.

THE BODY'S MOVING FRAMEWORK

An understanding of the framework of the body will make it easier for you to understand human movement. Picture a modern-day factory under construction. It looks like a large version of a child's metal building set.

Your body framework is very similar to this steel structure, but the steel girders have been replaced by bones.

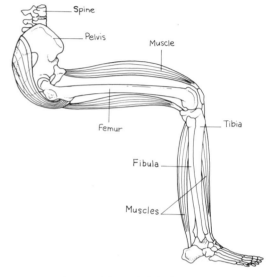

A side view of the pelvis and right leg

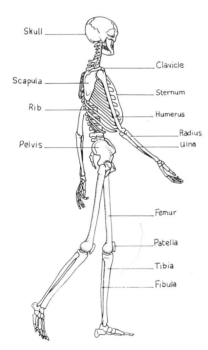

The human skeleton

Bones and girders do the same job—they give shape, they give support and they protect what is inside.

The **skeletal framework** is made up of bones and joints. Many bones have muscles attached to them. Together they combine to:
a) support the body (so it can stand, sit, etc.);
b) allow movement.

In addition to muscles, the skeletal framework also has the following:

● ligaments;
● tendons;
● cartilage;
● synovial fluid (in joints).

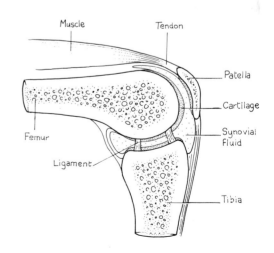

A section through the knee joint

JOINTS AND HOW THEY MOVE

Cartilage covers the ends of the bones and helps a joint to cope with stress and strain by reducing friction between the bones. In the knee joint there are also flat shaped discs of cartilage between the bones.

Synovial fluid is a thin liquid produced to help lubricate a joint and further reduce friction.

Ligaments are made of strong tissue and join one bone to another. Ligaments bind a joint together and prevent it over-stretching or even dislocating.

Tendons are made of a similar tough tissue but have a different purpose. A tendon joins a muscle to a bone and plays an important part in movement. The end of the tendon attached to the bone which remains relatively still is known as the **origin**, and the end attached to the bone which moves is known as the **insertion**.

As a muscle contracts it shortens, and as the tendon is attached to the bone (as well as the muscle) it will pull the bone closer. For example, in the diagram, the forearm is raised as the **biceps** muscle contracts. At the same time the **triceps** muscle relaxes. The opposite happens as the elbow straightens.

An understanding of the skeletal framework is best gained from examining one simple skill, and observing how muscles, bones, ligaments and tendons work together.

TASK

Note: it is best to have a bare arm for this task.
1. Hold a light weight (3–5 kg) in your left hand, keeping your arm hanging down straight.
2. Bend your arm slowly at the elbow to lift the weight up to your shoulder. Use your right hand to feel how the muscles in your left arm are working.

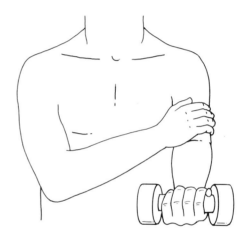

Points to notice
Muscle 1 becomes fatter and shorter (it is now contracting).
Muscle 2 becomes thinner and longer (it is now relaxing).
The tendon is easy to feel at the elbow.

This is what happens when the weight is lifted.

- As muscle 1 tenses and contracts (becomes shorter and fatter), muscle 2 gradually relaxes (becomes longer and thinner).
- As muscle 1 contracts and shortens, it pulls the tendon fixed to the forearm. This makes the arm bend, which lifts the weight.
- To lower the weight, muscle 1 and muscle 2 work together—*they share the workload*.
- The ligaments at the elbow keep the joint secure throughout the movement.

Scapula

Contraction of biceps raises forearm

Biceps (muscle 1)

Triceps (muscle 2)

Humerus

Radius   Ulna

A side view of the right forearm being raised

All voluntary movement is the result of muscles contracting—becoming shorter.

A muscle that is responsible for movement is called a **prime mover** or **agonist**. It usually has another muscle working in the opposite direction. The opposite muscle is known as the **antagonistic** muscle.

When lifting a weight, the biceps is the prime mover and the triceps is the antagonist.

Many muscles in the body not only help movement, but maintain posture (they support the body against the force of gravity and keep it in the correct upright position).

TASK 2

Choose a skill, or part of a skill, and work out how the muscles work together to allow the skill to be performed.

BASIC SKELETAL MOVEMENT

By examining the skill of kicking, we can see how muscles, bones and tendons work together to create **flexion** and **extension** in the knee joint.

The muscles at the back of the thigh contract, and those at the front relax. The lower leg is pulled back and up. When the joint angle becomes smaller we refer to the movement as **flexion**.

Flexion of the knee

Extension of the knee

Just before contact with the ball, the muscles at the back of the thigh relax, and those at the front contract. This causes a quick **extension** of the knee joint (straightening of the leg). Extension is the return movement from flexion.

There are two other types of basic movements. **Abduction** is a movement away from the midline of the body. **Adduction** is the return movement from abduction.

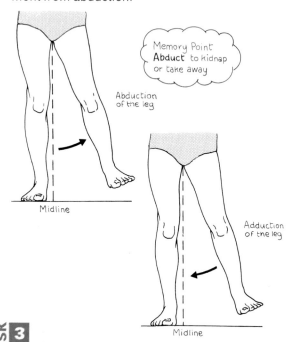

Memory Point
Abduct to kidnap or take away

Abduction of the leg

Midline

Adduction of the leg

Midline

TASK 3

Analyse the breast stroke leg kick in terms of flexion, extension, abduction and adduction.

SUMMARY

Muscles, **bones**, **tendons** and **ligaments** make up the skeletal framework.

The skeletal framework allows movement to take place, and supports the body against the force of gravity.

Where movement takes place, it is the result of groups of muscles working together—one muscle contracts while another relaxes, whilst others stabilise the joint.

Flexion is a movement where the joint angle becomes smaller.

Extension is the return movement from flexion.

Abduction is a movement away from the midline of the body.

Adduction is a return movement from abduction.

CONTROLLING YOUR MOVEMENT

Run ... Walk ... Hop ... Jog ... Step ... Catch ... Throw ... Hit ... Jump ... Twist ... Roll ... Hit ... Dive. All physical activities involve movement. To find out in more detail how and why the body moves, try a standing broad jump as described below.

TASK 1

1. Stand with your feet together.
2. Jump as far as you can, throwing your arms forward as you jump.

The broad jump

How does your body perform that skill? Your **brain** passes the message to your **nervous system**, which in turn gives messages to your **muscles**, which move your **bones**.

MUSCLES, THE SKELETON AND THE NERVOUS SYSTEM

Let's look again at the standing broad jump; this time focussing on the leg, especially the muscles of the thigh and the action of the knee joint.

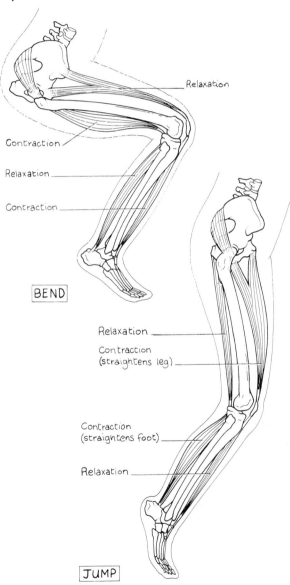

The action of the leg muscles involved in the broad jump

QUESTIONS AND ANSWERS

Q: What starts the movement of the standing broad jump?

A: The **brain**.

Q: How does the brain take in, and respond to, what is going on around it?

A: Through the **nervous system**.

Q: What is the nervous system?

A: It is a **communication system** along which messages in the form of **nerve impulses** are sent.

Q: What do nerve impulses do?

A: Nerve impulses control body movement. Without nerve impulses, the skeletal muscles are unable to contract (become shorter).

Q: What happens when a skeletal muscle receives a nerve impulse and contracts?

A: Part of the body moves.

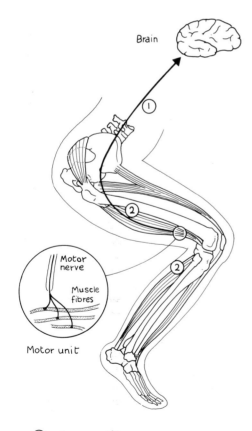

Brain

Motor nerve

Muscle fibres

Motor unit

① Central nervous system

② Peripheral nervous system

THOUGHT SPOT

Now think about the ready position (position 1) in the standing jump. How does the brain send nerve impulses to the muscles of the thigh?

INFO BOX

When we consider movement, we are only concerned with the **voluntary** nervous system— that's the part over which we have some control. The other system in the body is known as the **autonomic** system and we have no control over it. For example, we cannot control our heartbeat.

TASK 2

Sit on a chair and cross one leg over the other at the knee, allowing the lower leg to hang down. Now tap your hanging leg just below the knee cap.

If you tap the correct spot, you should see the lower leg jerk involuntarily, that is without you having to deliberately think about the leg.

This movement is caused by what is called a **reflex action**—a quick, automatic response to a stimulus. Sneezing, coughing, blinking and the quick removal of your hand from a very hot object are other examples of reflex actions, which are controlled by the autonomic nervous system.

SUMMARY

All deliberate movement is a result of messages being sent by the brain through the **nervous system** to the **muscles**.

Messages are sent as **nerve impulses**.

Deliberate movement comes about through the **voluntary** nervous system over which we have control.

The **central nervous system** (CNS) includes the brain and the spinal cord.

The **peripheral nervous system** (PNS) includes all parts of the nervous system outside the CNS.

Reflex movements are automatic and are controlled by the **autonomic nervous system**.

WARM-UP AND COOL DOWN

The human body works automatically to maintain its normal temperature of 37°C (98.6°F). There are times, however, when you feel the need to be warmer, or cooler.

WHY WARM UP?

It is important to prepare your body for the strenuous work involved in taking part in an activity. Correctly done, this will help prevent injury to muscles, tendons and ligaments and improve flexibility. In addition, muscles react more quickly when they are warm.

WHY COOL DOWN?

After activity it is important to prepare your body for a resting (non-active) state. Cooling-down exercises can reduce the stiffness in muscles which is sometimes experienced after strenuous work.

WHAT IS A WARM-UP?

Quite simply, a warm-up is a planned series of exercises aimed at thoroughly preparing the body for the activity ahead. A warm-up usually has two stages.

Stage 1
Action: walking, jogging or light running. It is important to build up slowly, make sure exercise is light and lasts for at least five minutes.
Result: the heart rate increases, more blood and heat flows to the muscles, and heat is generated in the muscles as a result of chemical reactions in the muscle cells.

Stage 2
Action: movement and rotation of large muscle groups and joints, e.g. arms, shoulders, legs and hips.
Result: as the muscles become warmer they become more elastic; this improves joint flexibility and helps prevent injury. In addition, a warm muscle will contract more quickly. More vigorous exercise at a later stage will be less stressful.

There are three ways to do the action of Stage 2.

1. **Static** stretching—stretching to the limit of movement or start of discomfort.

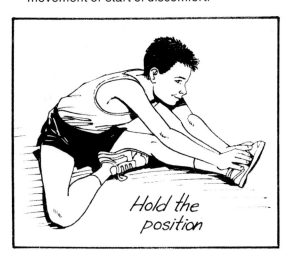

Hold the position

2. **Dynamic** stretching—this is more rapid and vigorous, e.g. arm circling. This is not recommended until the body warms up.

3. Partner help—a partner may help you stretch but this should be done carefully and always under supervision.

THOUGHT SPOT

How often have you warmed up using stretching? Do you use one method more than another?

In some activities, there may also be a third stage which involves practising the actions or movements required (for example, practising a golf swing).

INFO BOX

One of the ways in which the brain controls body temperature is by sending messages to the blood vessels via the autonomic nervous system. For example, if the body is too warm, blood vessels in the skin are instructed to open wider. More blood can then flow close to the surface of the skin and heat is lost to the surroundings. If the body is too cold the blood vessels get a message to become narrower.

THE 'COOL DOWN'

Avoid ending vigorous exercises or activity suddenly. The cool-down period should last a few minutes, with the level of exercise reducing slowly. It may include some light and easy stretching. This helps remove waste products from the muscles and reduces stiffness.

SUMMARY

A **physical warm-up** is important before any physical activity. It should be gradual and progressive. It should include running, stretching and practice of skill movements.
A warm-up prepares the body for the activity, improves performance and helps to prevent injury.
A warm-up also helps to improve flexibility.
A '**cool down**' after activity prepares the body for a resting state. This can involve a series of gentle exercises and stretching.

FITNESS OVERVIEW

As you know from Unit 1, there are three differ-ent *types* of fitness—**strength**, **stamina** and **flex-ibility**. To lead a healthy and active life you need to have some of each type. This is known as **health-related fitness** (HRF).

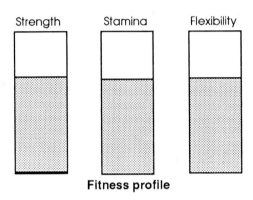

Fitness profile

There are also different *levels* of fitness, which we will call 'low', 'medium' and 'high'.

To take part in an activity at a high level, you will need higher levels of one or more of each type of fitness. This is known as **performance-related fitness** (PRF). For example, a weightlifter re-quires mainly strength, so his profile might look like this:

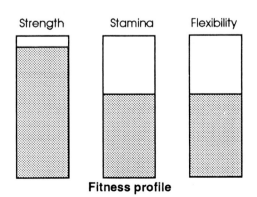

Fitness profile

TASK 1

Look at the fitness profiles below. One belongs to a middle-distance runner and the other to a ballet dancer. Which is which?

? Ballet dancer

? Middle-distance runner

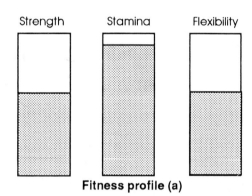

Fitness profile (a)

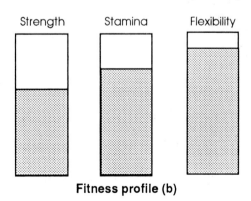

Fitness profile (b)

TASK 2

Some activities need high levels of more than one type of fitness, for example strength and flexibility. Can you think of examples?

TRAINING PROGRAMMES

Fitness is best improved through regular training. The different types of fitness (strength, stamina and flexibility) need different training programmes.

Fitness will improve if you:

● increase how often you train (the **frequency**);
● increase the time you spend training (the **duration**);
● increase how hard you train (the **intensity**).

This is the **principle of overload**.

TASK 3

Think of any training programme in which you have taken part. How did your teacher or coach apply the principle of overload? What changes took place in the training programme over a four-week period?

TESTING FITNESS

It is important to have an accurate measure of your level of fitness. There are many different tests of physical fitness but they all attempt to measure the following features.

1. **Strength**—strong muscles increase in size. Strength is your ability to move or hold a weight or resistance.
2. **Flexibility**—how far you can stretch.
3. **Stamina**—as muscles become fitter, they are able to keep working for longer periods.

A CLOSER LOOK AT STAMINA

There are two ways of looking at stamina. When one part of the body (one muscle group) is asked to do a strenuous task for a long time, we call it **muscular endurance**. Alternatively, when the whole body works for a long time it is known as **cardiovascular endurance**. As your cardiovascular endurance improves, your heart becomes stronger. (See Units 27–29.)

In squash, for example, constant use of the arm improves muscular endurance while continuous movement about the court improves cardiovascular endurance.

A strong, fit heart has many advantages over a weak, unfit heart:

● it can pump out more blood to the working muscles with each beat;
● it need not beat as often in supplying the same amount of blood;
● it recovers more quickly after exercise;
● it beats more slowly at rest (resting pulse rate).

TASK 4

Study the graphs and answer the questions which follow. The answers are all contained in this unit.

1. Why is the resting heart rate of the unfit runner higher than that of the fit runner?
2. Why is the heart rate of the unfit runner higher after five minutes than that of the fit runner after the same length of time?
3. Why does the heart rate of the unfit runner take so long to return to normal?

INFO BOX

When asked to work hard, an unfit person may quickly build up what is called an **oxygen debt**— the body is unable to supply enough oxygen, from breathing, for the muscles to work. After exercise, the person will often continue to breathe heavily in order to replace oxygen used during the exercise.

TASK 5

Try a five-minute run. Measure your pulse before and after the exercise. (If you don't know how, ask your teacher to show you.)

INFO BOX

The average 'resting pulse' for an adult is 70 beats per minute. However, some top athletes may have a resting pulse as low as 36 beats per minute!

Your pulse has a potential maximum of 220 minus your age—you would need to work very hard to achieve this. Normally, a training pulse is between 130 and 160 beats when overloading is taking place.

See Unit 29 for further information.

The graphs below represent the change in heart rate of a fit and an unfit runner during and after a five-minute run.

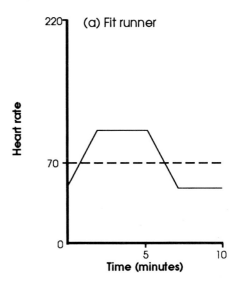

(a) Fit runner

Heart rate · Time (minutes)

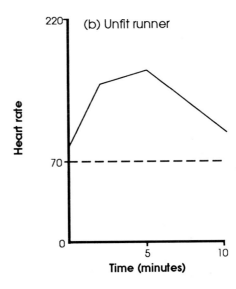

(b) Unfit runner

Heart rate · Time (minutes)

⚠ SAFETY NOTE

Young people must be careful not to 'overdo' their training programme.

Young bodies are still growing and developing, and are often not strong enough to cope with too much physical work.

Training programmes for young people must be carefully designed by someone who is qualified to do so.

FITNESS EXTRA

Some people argue that being fit for an activity means more than just being strong, having stamina, or being flexible. They ask: 'What about fast reactions, balance, coordination, and agility?'

1. Fast Reactions
Reaction time measures how quickly you move after a signal such as a starting pistol in a race. Here are the reaction times for the athletes who finished in the first four places in the 1988 Olympic Games 100 metres final for men.

Athlete	Reaction Time*
Ben Johnson	0.132 second
Carl Lewis	0.136 second
Linford Christie	0.138 second
Calvin Smith	0.176 second

*Time taken from the firing of the starter's pistol to the moment when the athlete explodes off the blocks (measured electronically).

❗ THOUGHT SPOT
In this race, what was the relationship between the reaction time of each athlete and his finishing position?

2. Balance
Keeping your balance means not falling over. Windsurfers need good balance if they are to stay on their boards.

3. Coordination
A person with good coordination can link their senses to body movements with ease.

In order to catch a ball you must be able to coordinate the position of your arms and hands with information about the flight of the ball (what you see).

4. Agility
Agility means being able to change direction accurately and quickly, and often involves starting and stopping.

TASK 6
List as many activities as you can where it would be to your advantage to:
a) have fast reactions;
b) have good balance;
c) have good coordination;
d) be agile.

❗ THOUGHT SPOT
Do you think that reaction time, balance, coordination and agility are parts of fitness?

SUMMARY

Fitness means **strength**, **stamina** and **flexibility**. Some people would also say it includes **balance**, **coordination**, **reaction time** and **agility**.
Levels of fitness vary between individuals.
Fitness levels can be measured and improved.
High levels of fitness are required in some physical activities.

FLEXIBILITY

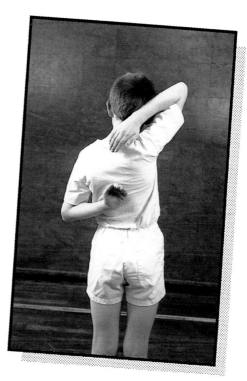

Flexibility is the **range of movement** at a **joint**. Good flexibility helps us perform skills better.

 TASK 1

Carry out the following three flexibility tests.

1. Shoulders
   a) Stand upright. Lift your right elbow as high as you can and reach down your back with your right hand.
   b) Let your left elbow point down and reach up with your left hand to touch your right hand.
   c) If you can get your hands to touch, you have quite a good range of movement in your shoulders.
   d) Compare your range of movement with that of other people.

2. Shoulders (again!)
    a) Sit down on the floor with your legs bent and feet flat on the ground.
    b) Put both arms out behind you; keep them straight, with your hands shoulder-width apart.
    c) Keep your hands where they are, and move your body slowly away from your hands. (Move your bottom, then feet, then bottom . . .)
    d) When you cannot slide any further, you have reached the end of the range of movement for your shoulders.
    e) Compare your range of movement with that of other people.

3. Hips and back
    You will need a partner to help you with this flexibility test.
    a) Sit down on the floor with your legs straight.
    b) Reach your hands forward and past your toes (if possible).
    c) Hold that stretch for two seconds, and ask a friend to measure either how far short of your toes or how far past your toes you have reached.

If you fail to reach your toes, your score will be a 'minus' one, e.g. −4 cm.

If you reach past your toes, your score will be a 'plus' one, e.g. +3 cm.

TASK 2

Look at the pictures below. Why is the range of movement important? Where is the flexibility required?

IMPROVING YOUR FLEXIBILITY

The best way to improve flexibility is to improve the **stretchibility** of the muscles.

1. A slow static stretch is best. Move slowly into the stretch.
2. Avoid 'bobbing' or 'bouncing' stretches (to avoid injury).
3. Stretch as far as you can without feeling pain.
4. Hold the position for 10–20 seconds.
5. Repeat the exercise five times.
6. For best results stretching should be done every day.
7. Before attempting any flexibility exercises, do a whole body warm-up, to warm the muscles by increasing the blood supply.
8. Muscles can be stretched '**passively**'. If you relax, a partner can move the body part for you. Once the end of the range of movement has been reached, this stretch is held for a few seconds. It is very important *not to over-stretch* with this form of stretching.

INFO BOX

Flexibility decreases with age, and through inactivity.

Flexibility can be reduced in cold temperatures. If you stretch a muscle suddenly, a reflex causes it to contract. Slow stretching does not trigger the '**stretch reflex**' and is therefore a better way of improving flexibility than sudden stretching or bobbing/bouncing.

HOW IS FLEXIBILITY RESTRICTED?

1. By the joint: for example the knee joint, which can only bend one way. It is a hinge joint, and opens and closes like the hinge of a door. The structure of the joint prevents any other movement.

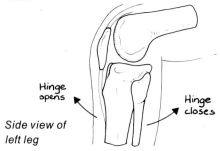

Hinge opens

Hinge closes

Side view of left leg

However, the shoulder joint does not have the same restrictions, because it is a different type of joint (a ball and socket).

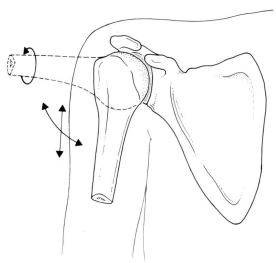

Front view of right shoulder

2. By fat or muscle: for example if you bend your elbow, your forearm eventually comes up against your biceps muscle and cannot go any further. If that muscle was bigger you would not have the same range of movement. Fat has the same effect.

3. By stretchibility: i.e. if the muscles which must stretch are very tight, then the range of movement is decreased. For example, when touching your toes, if the muscles in the backs of your thighs are sore it is because they cannot stretch enough to allow the movement to take place.

🛈 THOUGHT SPOT

What might happen to a gymnast with poor flexibility in the lower back?

SUMMARY

Flexibility is the range of movement at a joint.
Flexibility is important because it helps the performance of a skill.
Flexibility is restricted by the type of joint, and the extensibility (stretching ability) of muscles and tendons.
Flexibility can be improved through regular stretching.
Inactivity reduces flexibility.

YOUR BODY'S FOOD REFINERY AND POWER SOURCE

UNIT 25

Examples of proteins: fish, meat, poultry, eggs, cheese, milk, cereals, bread, peanuts.
Used for: building and repairing tissues, supplying energy.

The swimmer is moving because certain muscles are contracting and then relaxing in a controlled way.

Petrol powers the car engine—but what powers the contraction of a muscle?

Your body does not have an engine, but millions of individual muscle cells which work together to allow a muscle to contract. In order to fully understand how body movement is fuelled, we must know how energy is stored and then released by each muscle cell.

Examples of fats: butter and cream, whole milk, salad oils, cooking fats.
Used for: supplying a large amount of energy in a small amount of food, and storing energy in fat stores in the body.

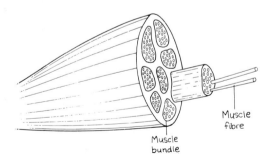

Muscle fibre

Muscle bundle

Human beings get their basic fuel from the food they eat in the form of **proteins**, **fats** and **carbohydrates**.

Examples of carbohydrates: breads and cereals, fruit, sugar, potatoes.
Used for: supplying energy.

Like the car engine, which cannot produce power from oil until it is refined into petrol, the body cannot use the energy held in foods until it too is further refined into a fuel—called **adenosine triphosphate** (ATP). Final refining is done by the digestive system and each cell.

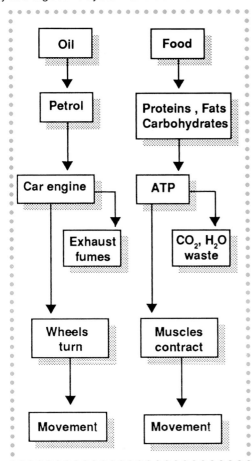

The biggest problem with ATP as a fuel is that it can only be stored in very small quantities. (That's just like having a very small petrol tank in a car.) This means that the cells are always at work producing ATP from carbohydrates, fats and proteins.

BREAKING DOWN CARBOHYDRATES

This is sometimes called **carbohydrate metabolism**. Carbohydrates are stored in the cells of the body in the form of **glycogen**. When energy is required, the glycogen combines with oxygen to produce ATP. This is known as **aerobic energy** (aerobic means 'with oxygen').

However, if the body is having to work very hard and there is not enough time for the body to supply enough oxygen, ATP can still be produced **anaerobically** (without oxygen). The disadvantage with this form of energy production is that a waste product called **lactic acid** is produced and muscle contraction will be forced to slow down or stop.

Fats and proteins can only be used as an energy source **aerobically** (with oxygen).

TASK **1**

Which athlete would require more aerobic endurance?
Why?

Said Aouita

Carl Lewis

ENERGY PRODUCTION

The three systems (digestive, circulatory and respiratory) are inter-related and rely upon each other to maintain the well-being of the individual.

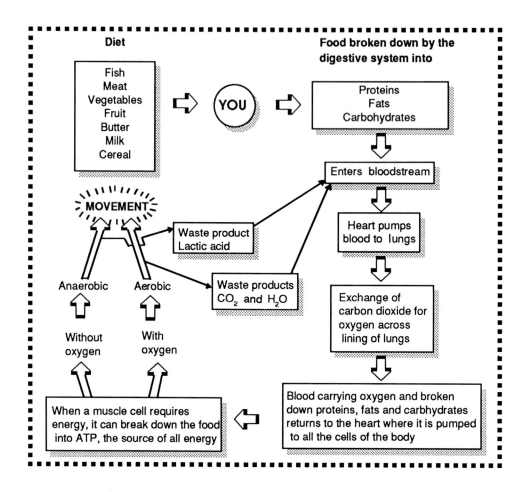

SUMMARY

The energy source for all performers is food. There are three main types of food which give energy: **proteins**, **fats** and **carbohydrates**.

These foods are broken down into ATP, which the cells can use to produce energy.

Carbohydrates are stored in the cells as **glycogen**.

Proteins, fats and glycogen can also be broken down into ATP with oxygen for energy production—this is known as **aerobic** respiration. Carbon dioxide (CO_2) and water are the waste products of aerobic respiration.

Glycogen can be broken down into ATP without oxygen, for anything up to 60 seconds—this is **anaerobic** respiration. **Lactic acid** is the waste product of anaerobic respiration.

Activities can be considered as aerobic or anaerobic depending on their duration and energy demands.

Aerobic respiration can continue as long as there is a supply of fuel (ATP) and oxygen.

THE OXYGEN TRANSPORT SYSTEM

The way oxygen is moved round the body to where it is needed is of great importance to most sportspeople. If the 'oxygen transport system' is improved, the body's ability to exercise over long periods is increased. To help us understand how the oxygen transport system works, let's consider the Acme Haulage Company and its distribution and return system between factory and shops.

The Acme Haulage Company delivers 'Oxy' (a product to be sold) to shops. A waste product 'Carbo' is left in a shop every time 'Oxy' is sold. The shops do not have a lot of storage space, and rely on 'Oxy' being regularly delivered and 'Carbo' regularly uplifted.

ACME DISTRIBUTION SYSTEM

Route 1   A lorry leaves the Acme distribution centre to pick up 'Oxy' at the exchange company and return 'Carbo'. It returns to the distribution centre before setting off on route 2.

Route 2   The lorry leaves the distribution centre to supply the shops with 'Oxy' and to pick up 'Carbo'. After supplying all the shops on its delivery run, the lorry returns to the distribution centre. When Acme are meeting the demands of the shops they refer to it as 'steady state working'. If demand increases, Acme can speed up the system, and after a time can keep that increased level going at a steady rate.

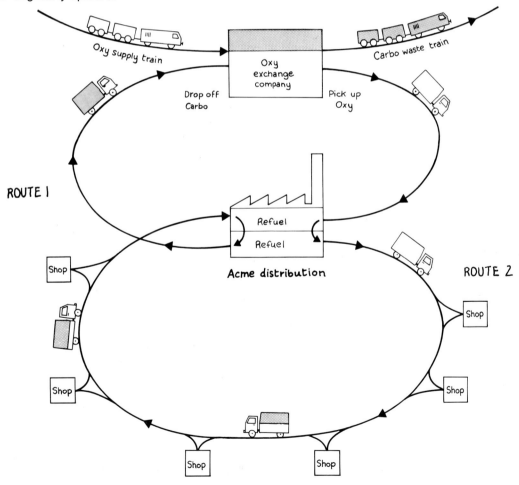

73

With others, act out the Acme distribution system.

If the demand for 'Oxy' is high, Acme refuel the lorries more quickly and send them out on the road faster. But if demand outstrips supply, and the shops use up their stock of 'Oxy', 'Carbo' takes up all the available space and the company refers to this as 'Oxy debt'. This forces the shops to close until the lorry arrives with new supplies of 'Oxy' and takes away the 'Carbo'. This happens during what the company calls the 'recovery period'.

THE BODY'S TRANSPORT SYSTEM

The oxygen transport system of the body is identical to the distribution system described. All we need do is change some of the names used in the diagram and text, i.e. replace:

- Acme Distribution Centre with the **heart**;
- 'Oxy' Exchange Company with the **lungs**;
- 'Carbo' with **carbon dioxide**;
- the shops with **muscle cells**;
- the lorries with **blood**;
- 'Oxy' with **oxygen**;
- Supply and Waste Trains with **breathing in** and **breathing out**.

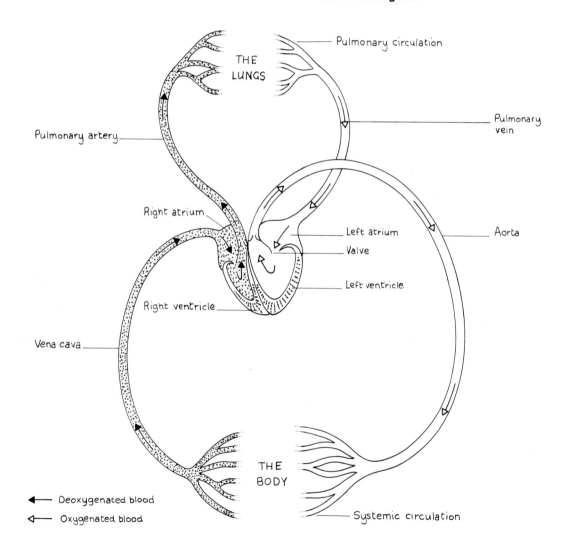

74

What do the routes represent in the human body?

Route 1, from the Acme distribution centre to the Oxy exchange company and back, represents the **pulmonary circulation**, from the heart to the lungs and back to the heart.

Route 2, from the Acme distribution centre to the shops and back, represents the **systemic circulation**, from the heart to the cells of the body requiring oxygen and back to the heart.

THE EFFECT OF TRAINING ON THE HEART AND LUNGS

Through a regular and well-planned training programme, the respiration and circulation systems can benefit in the following ways.

1. Increased **vital capacity**—the vital capacity of your lungs is the total amount of air that you can breathe in, in one breath.

a) The average vital capacity of adult men is between 4 and 5 litres; the figure for women is 3 to 4 litres. Some top class marathon runners, cyclists and cross-country skiers have vital capacities of between 7 and 8 litres.

b) A large vital capacity will allow you to take in more air with fewer and deeper breaths, thereby preventing fatigue.

2. Increased **stroke volume**—stroke volume is the quantity of blood pushed out by the heart with every beat/stroke.

a) A trained athlete's stroke volume is greater than a non-trained person.

b) The heart rate of a trained athlete will be lower than that of a non-trained person when both perform the same physically demanding work.

3. The heart rate of a trained athlete will return to its normal resting rate after physically demanding work more quickly than the heart rate of an untrained person, that is they will pay back their 'oxygen debt' more quickly than an untrained person.

Note: training to improve cardiovascular fitness will be hindered if the person smokes. Smoking damages the lungs and blood vessels, making it more difficult for oxygen to be taken in and transferred to the working muscles.

TASK **2**

Using the diagram of the Acme Haulage Company's distribution system as an example of your **cardio-respiratory system**, answer the following questions.

1. What is the effect on muscle cells if the demand for oxygen outstrips the supply?
2. If these cells keep going are they working aerobically or anaerobically?
3. What would be the effect on the body if the ability of the lungs to transfer oxygen into the system were cut in half?
4. If the heart was trained to be able to work harder and better, how might the body benefit?

SUMMARY

Circulation and respiration work together to supply oxygen to the muscles.

When air is breathed in, oxygen is transferred across the surfaces of the lungs into the blood and is carried back to the heart. As the blood is picking up O_2, it also allows CO_2 to be transferred back into the lungs to be breathed out— this circulation route is called the **pulmonary circulation route**.

The blood carrying the oxygen (which is attached to red blood cells) is pumped round the body to the muscle cells in the **systemic circulation route**.

DEVELOPING CARDIOVASCULAR ENDURANCE

Muhammed
Age : 17
Final year at school
wants to go to
University next year.
Interests : Music,
disco dancing
reading athletics.

Jenny
Age : 15
Fourth year at school
wants to become
an engineer
Interests : Netball
football, watching
television, athletics.

Muhammed and Jenny reached the County Cross-country finals without having seriously trained for athletics. At that meeting, they were spotted by a well known coach who recognized their potential and invited them to attend one of her coaching sessions.

Coach: 'Hello, Jenny. Hello, Muhammed.'

Jenny: 'Hello Ms Boxer. Thanks for inviting us to come to your session tonight. To be honest, we've never trained seriously for athletics before.'

Coach: 'That's what excites me so much about your potential. If you did train, I think you could both improve enough to reach the National Championships.'

Muhammed: 'Can training really make that much difference to how fast we run?'

Coach: 'Of course it can. Before I set you any training programmes, I will explain how **endurance training** works.'

The pupils are both cross-country runners. This is an **aerobic** activity which you will remember from Unit 25 means that the energy required for performance comes from glycogen and oxygen. In the remainder of this unit, we will look at the advice offered by the coach.

IMPROVING AEROBIC FITNESS

Step 1   Calculate your resting heart rate.

TASK **1**

Work with a partner. Use the forefinger and middle finger of one hand to find your pulse. Over a 15-second period, count the number of 'blimps' you feel beneath your finger tips. Multiply this number by 4. The answer is your resting heart rate.

Step 2   Calculate your maximal heart rate.

TASK

Do this by subtracting your age from 220:

$$220 - age = maximal\ heart\ rate.$$

(Jenny is 15, so her maximal heart rate is 205 beats per minute.)

To improve **aerobic** fitness, an athlete must train hard enough to keep the heart beating at between 70% and 85% of maximal heart rate. This is called the **training zone**. Jenny's training zone is therefore between

$$205 \times 0.70 = 144\ beats\ per\ minute$$
and
$$205 \times 0.85 = 174\ beats\ per\ minute$$
(note rounding up of figures).

For an aerobic improvement to take place, Jenny must keep her heart rate within the training zone for at least 20 minutes.

TASK **3**

Work out your own training zone and plot it on a graph.

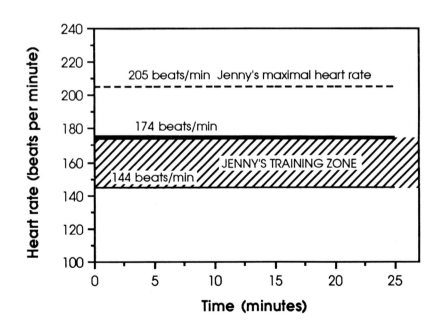

The coach explained how to improve aerobic endurance to Muhammed and Jenny, then she asked if they had any questions.

Muhammed: 'How often and for how long each time are we going to have to train to improve our endurance?'

Coach: 'Usually the best number of training sessions is three to four every week with sessions lasting between 20 and 40 minutes. Throughout each training session we will try to keep your heart beat within your training zone. Of course, sometimes it will drop and sometimes it will rise, but it will average out around 75% of your maximal heart rate.'

Jenny: 'What sort of sessions will you be asking us to do?'

Coach: 'There will generally be two types. Firstly, you will do a variety of distance runs—where you run for 20–40 minutes at a speed which makes your heart reach its training rate. And secondly, you'll do some interval training, sometimes called Fartlek Training. With this you work for periods where your heart rate reaches almost its maximal rate; there are rest periods however, where your heart rate will drop down to 120 beats a minute. The important thing about these sessions is that they will average out at your **training heart rate**. Now you understand something about what you are going to be doing, let's go down to the track and do some real work.'

Cardiovascular endurance can be improved by training at high altitude. This encourages the body to produce more red blood cells. When the athlete returns to sea level, the extra red blood cells increase the amount of oxygen which can be transported in the blood, and this improves endurance.

An illegal process known as **blood doping** has a similar effect to high altitude training. This can involve a pint of blood being taken from the athlete several weeks before a competition; the body automatically replaces the 'lost' blood. Just before the competition, the stored blood is injected back into the athlete's bloodstream, the result being an increase in the number of red blood cells.

TASK 4

Answer these questions.

1. When setting out a training programme, why must level of fitness and age be considered first?
2. Why is fitness training to music sometimes called 'aerobics'?

TASK 5

Calculate the training pulse rates for a 20-year-old, a 35-year-old and a 50-year-old.

INFO BOX

Things which affect endurance are:
a) pace—an even pace is best;
b) level of skill—a skilled person wastes little energy;
c) sex—the endurance of women is less than men;
d) age—endurance increases up to the age of 20–25, after which it decreases;
e) heat—high temperatures can cause 'heat stress' and restrict endurance.

SUMMARY

Aerobic fitness is improved when an athlete's **training heart rate** (equal to 75% of maximal heart rate) is maintained for 20 minutes.
Athletes should train three to four times per week for maximum benefit.
Training sessions are usually of two types:
a) 20–40 minutes at your training rate;
b) interval training.
Pace, level of skill, sex, age, heat and altitude can affect endurance.

STRENGTH: MOVE IT OR HOLD IT

TYPES OF STRENGTH

There are two types of strength.

1. **Static isometric**—this is where *no* movement takes place, as in the photograph opposite of the gymnast.

The *bigger* a muscle, the *stronger* it is. It is possible to increase muscle size through hard physical work. If you increase muscle size, you increase **strength**.

In the past, people developed their strength through their daily work. Many jobs were very physically demanding, e.g. farming, forestry, mining. Nowadays, many jobs do not involve the same amount of physical work because machines have replaced human effort.

TO APPLY FORCE

Muscle strength is the capacity of a muscle to exert force against a **resistance**. It is usually measured by one attempt to push or hold as much as possible.

2. **Dynamic isotonic**—this is where movement does take place as in the photograph above of the weightlifter.

Dynamic strength is used far more often in physical activities.

INFO BOX

Strength is usually measured by one maximum contraction.

Strength is the foundation for muscular endurance and power (see Units 29 and 30).

Strength improves muscle tone and form.

Strength is the foundation for proper posture.

Strength around the joints can help prevent injury.

TASK 1

Test your strength by:
a) arm-wrestling a partner;
b) attempting a one-arm press-up.

People can increase their strength through some form of **fitness training**. The amount of strength training required depends on the chosen sport or physical activity. Here are some activities where strength is important:

Rugby	Soccer
American football	Basketball
Athletics	Gymnastics
Weightlifting	Dance

TASK 2

1. Name three skills which use static isometric strength.
2. Name three skills which use dynamic isotonic strength.
3. The digging machine has replaced manual digging. Name four other jobs where machines have replaced man power.
4. Test your strength with a grip dynamometer.

❗ MEMORY HELPER

Isotonic and isometric may both be new words for you. You may find it difficult to remember which one means static, and which means dynamic (involving movement). Try this: **isotonic** has two letter 'o's—think of this as the 'oo' sound in 'movement'.

INFO BOX

A person's strength reaches its maximum round the age of 20 for women and 25 for men. A person loses approximately 1% of his/her strength every year after the maximum. The rate of strength loss is related to activity level.

An average man is 30–35% stronger than an average woman of the same age. A man's muscles are generally larger than those of a woman.

A diet which is low on protein makes it difficult to maintain or improve strength (see Unit 25).

SUMMARY

If you increase muscle size you increase strength.
Strength is defined as the ability of a muscle to exert force against a resistance.
In static/isometric strength, *no* movement takes place.
In dynamic/isotonic strength, movement does take place.
Age, diet and whether you are male or female, all have an effect on a person's strength.

DEVELOPING STRENGTH

Strength is a foundation for **muscular endurance** and **power**. All three aspects of fitness are of vital importance to people taking part in physical activities.

In many activities, performance can be affected if any one aspect is missing. Where any 'aspect of fitness' plays a part in an activity, it is possible to improve performance by **training** or **conditioning**. In this unit we will look at how strength can be improved through different forms of training or conditioning.

There are two stages in developing strength in a training programme.

Stage 1 The muscles must contract against a heavy resistance (e.g. a weight). The muscles are 'overloaded'—they do more work than normal.

Stage 2 The resistance (e.g. a weight) must be increased progressively as the muscles become stronger—this makes sure that the muscles are always 'overloaded'.

WAYS OF DEVELOPING STRENGTH

1. Bodyweight exercises, where the whole or part of the body is lifted, e.g. press-ups (dynamic/isotonic). There is a problem with bodyweight exercises: the difficulty of adding weight as the muscles become stronger (Stage 2 above). Bodyweight exercises are sometimes called **calisthenics**.

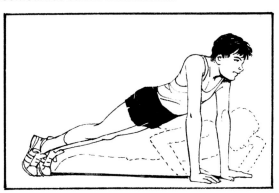

2. Exercises using mobile weights—this is a very good way to develop strength because the resistance can be increased progressively (dynamic/isotonic).

FOR SAFETY always have a spotter

3. Exercises where the muscles are tensed against something which cannot move, e.g. a door, or against another body part (static/isometric).

Note: there is another form of fitness training called **isokinetic**. This is similar to isotonic training where weights are *moved*, but by using special machines the **resistance** always equals the **muscular force**.

DYNAMIC (ISOTONIC) TRAINING

There are a variety of ways to develop strength using weights. The **bench press** is one example. This exercise develops the strength of muscles in the chest and upper arm.

The first thing the athlete does is to work out the *maximum* weight he/she can lift in *one repetition* (one complete action).

The best way to develop strength is to perform eight repetitions as near to maximum as possible. This is known as 'one set of eight repetitions' (reps). If the athlete had a maximum lift of 50 kg, then he/she might attempt three sets of eight repetitions with a 40 kg weight. He/she would rest for two minutes between sets.

Bench press: maximum 50 kg
40 kg × 8 reps × 3 sets

Arm curl: maximum 25 kg
20 kg × 8 reps × 3 sets

Fitness Card			
Name:			
Exercise	kg	Reps	Sets
1. Bench press	40	8	3
2. Arm curl	20	8	3

BOX

Training should take place every second day for best results.

The exercise should not be 'forced'.

Once the target strength is reached, there is no need to increase the resistance.

Strength gained slowly stays with the performer for a longer time than strength gained quickly.

Never hold your breath during a strength exercise, i.e.

- breathe out when applying force;
- breathe in during the recovery phase.

STATIC (ISOMETRIC) TRAINING

One example of an isometric exercise is standing in a doorway and pushing against the sides.

What to do:

a) hold the push for 5–10 seconds;

b) perform 6–8 repetitions at near maximal tension;

c) train every day;

d) note the change in your upper arm/shoulder/chest muscles.

1

Choose a physical activity, and select a skill which would improve if the strength of the performer were increased. Devise a strength training programme to improve that skill; go through all the stages of programme design. (Look back at the fitness card.)

SAFETY NOTE

Never train by yourself.

Ask a qualified person to show you how to use weights properly.

Always warm up before weight training.

Always 'warm down' after weight training.

Do not train with weights until your body is capable of using them properly (as a rough guide, about 16 years old).

SUMMARY

Strength is an important aspect of fitness as it can also help in the development of muscular endurance and power.

Strength can be improved in different ways.

Some training programmes use your body-weight, while others involve the use of weights.

Weight training programmes usually involve 'sets' of 'repetitions'.

Muscles must be **overloaded** by increasing the resistance or the repetitions.

As muscles become stronger the training programme should be increased progressively to ensure that muscles continue to be overloaded.

UNIT 30

MUSCULAR ENDURANCE

Muscular endurance is very closely related to strength. Muscular endurance is the ability to make repeated **muscular** contractions. Activities where muscular endurance is very important are swimming (repeated arm movement), canoeing (as for swimming) and trampolining (repeated leg movements).

Muscular endurance is measured either by the number of repetitions or the time a contraction is held.

INFO BOX

It is possible for a press-up to be a **strength exercise** for one person, and **muscular endurance exercise** for another.

People differ in their strength—remember this when devising any exercise programme.

Form of training	How to improve
Strength training	Add more weight to 'overload' the muscle
Muscular endurance training	Do more repetitions to 'overload' the muscle

Example

Julie struggles to do more than one pull-up. For Julie this would be a strength exercise, as it would be as much as she could manage (maximum muscle contraction). Katy can perform eight pull-ups, so one pull-up could not be a maximum muscle contraction.

Note: 'overload' means to make a muscle do more than normal. Strength training and muscular endurance training both **overload** the muscles. There are two main differences.

1. For **strength training** we use heavy weights and a low number of repetitions (6–12).
2. For **muscular endurance training** we use light weights and a high number of repetitions (over 20).

There are many ways of developing muscular endurance. One method is **circuit training**, which can also improve cardiovascular fitness.

CIRCUIT TRAINING

In this circuit, the **resistance** is the **bodyweight** of the performer.

A **circuit** is when you move round a series of exercises; if you go around the exercises *twice*, you perform two circuits. •

TASK 1

State which body part or muscle group is being worked in each exercise. Why are the exercises placed in this order?

There are two stages in setting up your own muscular endurance programme.

Stage 1 For each exercise test yourself to maximum, for 60 seconds.

Stage 2 Halve the number of reps you score; this equals the number of reps you will do in the circuit.

1. Press-ups
2. Bench jumps
3. Pull-ups
4. Trunk raises
5. Sit-ups
6. Step-ups

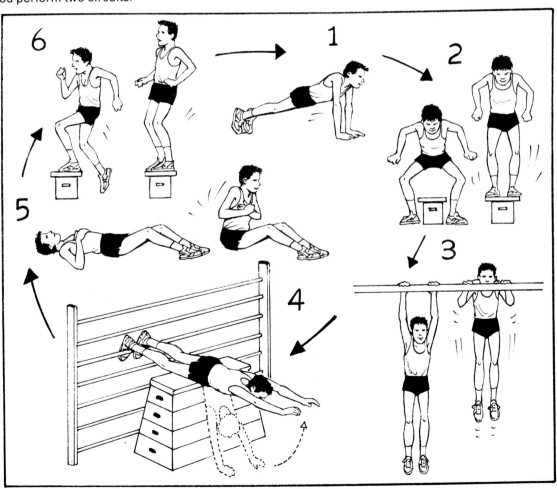

Example
Luke Rossi can perform 40 press-ups in one minute.
Half of 40 = 20; he will do 20 press-ups in each circuit.
It's a good idea to draw-up a **circuit card**. Luke's card is shown below. He completes three circuits every training day, and after one month he re-tests himself to maximum.

🛈 THOUGHT SPOT
What are the advantages of the circuit card?

Name: Luke Rossi	Class: 4 × 2		Training days: Mon p 1,2 Thurs p 6,7			
Exercise	Max	Reps	Max	Reps	Max	Reps
1. Press-ups	40	20				
2. Bench jumps	30	15				
3. Pull-ups	14	7				
4. Trunk raises	18	9				
5. Sit-ups	28	14				
6. Step-ups	40	20				

'Max' = the maximum number of repetitions in one minute.

'Reps' = the number of repetitions to be performed during each visit to an exercise.

Note: if your maximum is an odd number, add on one to make it even, then halve that number.

Example
41 reps at maximum is an odd number.
Add 1 to make it 42.
Half of 42 = 21 training reps.

After a month of training, Luke re-tested. His maximums were greater; the totals increased as he became fitter.

SUMMARY

Muscular endurance is the ability to make repeated muscular contractions.
Muscular endurance training usually involves light weights/resistance and a high number of repetitions.
Strength training usually involves heavy weights/resistance and a low number of repetitions.
Circuit training is a common way of developing muscular endurance.

POWER IS 'FAST STRENGTH'

1

4

3

2

In sporting activities we often hear the word 'power' being mentioned by commentators or coaches, but what are they really talking about? If you look at the four photographs above you might begin to get some idea about 'power'.

In 1 the goalkeeper is attempting to kick the ball a long distance.
In 2 the sprinter is trying to get away from his blocks as quickly as he can.

In 3 the gymnast has jumped as high as she can in the air so that she can perform a somersault before she lands.
In 4 the shot-putter pushes the shot as hard and as fast as she can.

What do all these skills have in common?

The answer is **power**.

We saw in Unit 28 that strength is the ability to move or hold against a resistance. If power can be called 'fast strength', then it must have something to do with the time it takes to move the resistance. Here is an easy way to demonstrate this.

1. Stand straight.
2. Bend your legs.
3A. Straighten your legs slowly.
3B. Straighten your legs as quickly as you can. (You should be able to jump into the air.)

In 3B, where you used your strength very quickly, you used more **power** than in 3A. Power is the rate at which you apply **strength**; the faster you apply your strength, the more power you are using.

INFO BOX

Speed equals the rate of movement of the whole body (or a body part).
Power is 'fast strength'; therefore
$$\text{power} = \text{force} \times \text{speed}.$$
Power can be increased by:
a) increasing force;
b) increasing speed (by improving the co-ordination of the skill and by correctly 'warming up' the muscles to be used).
Explosive power = almost maximum force × almost maximum speed.
Explosive power is demonstrated in many sporting activities, e.g. sprint start, shot putt, high jump.

TASK 1

Examine the photographs at the beginning of this unit again. Can you identify where the power is coming from for each skill?

TASK 2

Which of the following skills do *not* require explosive power? Discuss your answers with a partner, then with your teacher.

1. Golf swing (a drive)
2. High jump
3. Volleyball spike—the jump
4. Cross-country running
5. Arm-wrestling
6. Riding
7. Swimming breaststroke
8. Tennis serve
9. Triple jump
10. 400 metre running
11. Weightlifting
12. Leaping in dance

SUMMARY

Power is important in many physical activities.
Power = force × speed.
Explosive power = maximum force × maximum speed.

SPORTS INJURIES

Injuries can happen at all levels and in most activities; many are minor but others can be very serious. Few injuries are as serious as the example above, and with proper treatment full fitness can usually be regained, with the performer playing at the same level as before. However, if not treated correctly, some injuries may not heal properly and end up recurring again and again.

❗ SAFETY NOTE

Young people must be careful about the amount of exercise or training they do. Their bones are still growing, and too much stress or strain through overwork may lead to injuries.

PREVENTING INJURIES

Some injuries may be avoided if you make sure that you are:
a) fit enough for your chosen activity and warmed up (see Unit 22 for further information);
b) properly equipped;
c) playing according to the rules and regulations for the activity.

Accidents can still happen, however, and injuries usually occur for one of three reasons.

1. A sudden knock or blow as a result of a fall, collision or tackle.
2. The stress and strain of overuse of a body part.
3. Breaking the rules or taking too much of a risk.

BLISTERS, ABRASIONS AND CUTS

Blisters, abrasions and skin burns are usually caused by rubbing (friction). For example, if a runner's shoe does not fit correctly, it may rub against the skin and cause a blister; a sliding tackle in football can cause an abrasion; sliding down a rope can give you a skin burn.

All cuts, abrasions and skin burns should be cleaned before applying a dressing. If necessary, in order to stop bleeding, apply direct pressure on the wound with either your thumb or fingers.

MUSCLE INJURIES

The letters R.I.C.E. can help you to remember how to give first aid to a muscle injury.

R Rest the injured part immediately, apply ice.

I Ice will cool the injury, causing the blood vessels to narrow so that bleeding is reduced.

Never put ice directly onto the skin. Use an ice pack or a bag of ice cubes.
Never apply ice for more than 20 minutes at a time.

C Compressing the injury will close blood vessels and reduce bleeding. This can be done with a bandage even over an ice pack. Take care not to bandage too tightly in case you cut off the blood supply completely.

E Elevation will also slow down bleeding by reducing the amount of blood getting to the affected area.

Bruises

A blow to a muscle may cause a bruise. A bruise forms because blood leaks from damaged blood vessels into surrounding muscle tissue. The skin, which remains unbroken, turns a bluish-purple colour. R.I.C.E. treatment should be applied but in the case of severe injury, it may be necessary to have the injured part X-rayed to see if a bone is broken. Bruised muscles can take time to repair, and a gradual return to exercise is sometimes necessary.

Pulled muscles (strains)

A muscle will be pulled or strained if it cannot cope with the force on it. There will be a sudden, sharp pain at the site of the injury. A doctor should be consulted if the pain is severe in case the muscle has been torn.

Sprains

A sprain is an injury to the ligaments at a joint, such as the ankle. (Ligaments give support to a joint, by 'strapping' one bone to another.) Sprains occur as a result of sudden twisting or stretching. The joint will be painful and swollen. R.I.C.E. treatment should be given. Consult a doctor if the pain is severe or if the swelling has not reduced within a few days.

Damaged cartilage

Some joints have special pads of cartilage which act as a cushion between two bones. These can be damaged by wear and tear, or by turning too quickly or too far. Damage to cartilage is common in the knee joint. The injured knee will be very painful and held in a bent position.

Do not change the bent position of the knee or attempt to straighten it. Contact a doctor.

In some cases the cartilage may be removed by an operation and, although the knee will recover, the ability to take part in sport may be affected.

Tendons

Muscles which are continually kept tight can put strain on the tendon (the part which joins the muscle to bone). This can cause pain and swelling which is often relieved by rest. However, if a tendon is torn, an operation may be needed to stitch it back on to the muscle. Athletes, in races such as the 100 metres, occasionally rupture an Achilles tendon when they leave their blocks, because of the large forces on their legs as a result of the explosive sprint start.

INFO BOX

Tennis elbow results from overuse of tendons in the elbow. Overuse of tendons is not confined to either tennis or the elbow joint. Many sports people suffer such pain in other joints. Rest is the only cure.

Dislocation

This happens as a result of a bump or blow to a joint. A bone is forced out of position and ligaments may also be torn. The bone may even be broken. The joint will be painful and swollen, and you should not try to put it back into place. This is a job for a doctor.

MORE SERIOUS INJURIES

Medical help is always needed in the following cases.

Concussion

Concussion results from a blow to the head. The injured person may become unconscious or suffer loss of memory. If concussion is suspected, a player must stop immediately and medical attention sought. If serious, the skull may be fractured and there may be bleeding inside the head causing damage to the brain.

Fracture

A cracked or broken bone is often caused by a blow or stress in a fall. There are three main types.

1. Closed fractures where the skin is not broken.

2. Open fractures in which a bone is pushed through the skin.

3. Greenstick fractures in which the bone cracks halfway across and then splits some distance up its length—like a twig. This type is especially common in children.

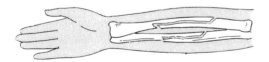

Take care in handling a person with a fracture and move the injured part as little as possible. If an injury to the spine is suspected, the person should not be moved.

TREATMENT OF INJURIES

The treatment of sports injuries is a job for medically trained people. Under no circumstances should an unqualified person attempt to treat a serious injury.

As well as doctors, physiotherapists are often involved in treating injuries. They use a variety of techniques including massage, ultrasound and gentle exercise.

If an injury is not treated properly, it may not heal fully. When the body part is later put under stress during physical activity, the injury may happen again. If an injury happens again and again, it is said to be **chronic**.

TASK 1

Contact someone who has suffered a serious injury. Find out what type of treatment was given.

SUMMARY

Despite the many precautions taken to make activities safe, accidents and injuries do happen. Some are minor and easily treated; others are more serious. Usually, full fitness is regained after treatment; however, some injuries prevent full fitness being regained. Most injuries require some form of treatment; in many cases, professional help is needed.

If an injury is not treated properly, it will not heal fully. If an injury happens again and again, it is said to be **chronic**. All performers should be careful not to return to training too soon in case an injury has not healed fully.

Young people must be particularly careful when exercising or taking part in an activity. If you overdo physical work or put great strain on your body, serious damage can occur that could affect you in later life.

INDEX

A abduction 58
adduction 58
administrators 6, 15
advertising 6
aerobic fitness 77
agility 66
alcohol 21
anabolic steroids 28
Anderson, Willie 29
anaerobic 71
amateur sportsperson 5, 30
apartheid 31
autonomic system 61, 62

B balance 41, 66
beta blockers 28
blood doping 28, 78
blood vessels 28
bones 56
boycott 30
British Olympic
  Association (BOA) 17
buoyancy 40

C carbon dioxide 74
cardio-respiratory system 75
cartilage 56, 96
Central Council of Physical
  Recreation (CCPR) 17
Centre of Gravity 41, 42, 43
cerebral palsy 19
choreographed 39
circulatory system 72
closed skill 33
coaches 6, 16, 28, 44, 51, 52
codes of conduct 10, 26
competition 30
Connelly, Harold 27
coordination 33, 46, 66
creativity 33

D Dalgado, Pedro 29
de Coubertin, Pierre 31
digestive system 72
disabled 17
dislocation 90
diuretics 27
drag 40
drugs 27, 28

E effectiveness 33
endurance 64
equipment 23
etiquette 11
extension 58

F fartlek training 78
feedback 48, 52
fitness 3, 63
flexion 58
flexibility 64
forces 40
fractures 91

G Gleneagles Agreement 31
glycogen 71

H heart rate 77

I injury, chronic 91
injury, risk 25
International Olympic
  Committee (IOC) 7
isometric 79
isotonic 79

J Johnson, Ben 27, 29
joints 47, 69
judge 26
judgement 33

L lactic acid 71, 72
ligaments 56, 57
local sports council 15

M media 27
mental preparation 44
motion 40
motivation 44
motor nerves 46
muscular contraction 70
muscular endurance 81, 84
muscles 47, 56, 61

N National Coaching Foundation 16
National Playing Fields
  Association (NPFA) 17
national residential centres 17
national teams 16
nervous system 59, 60
neurones 46

O officials 14
olympic games 7, 27, 31
open skill 33
overload 64
oxygen debt 65

P participation, reasons for 2, 4
performers 14, 17, 36, 37,
          38, 48, 55

personality 45
physical contact 26
physical preparation 44
power 87
power to weight ratio 54

R reaction time 33, 66
referee 26
reflex action 60
resistance 23, 79
respiratory system
          72, 73, 74, 75
rules 9, 11

S sensory pathway 46
Sheldon 53
skeleton 56
skills 3
somatotypng 53
special needs 18
spectators 6, 11, 20
speed 54
sponsor 6
sports asociations 6
sports centres 6
Sports Council 16, 28, 30
sportsmanship 11
sprains 90
stamina 64
stimulants 28
strength 54, 64
stress 45
stretching 61
support staff 6
synovial fluid 56

T systemic circulation 75
tactics 16, 49
technique 35, 36
tendons 47, 56, 61
third world countries 30
timing 33
toxic poisoning 28
training, principles 64
training, pulse 64
training, zone 77

U umpire 26

V vital capacity 75
voluntary movement 58

W wheelchair basketball 19
winning,
  importance of 4, 30